ELEM

Al

by
F. A. WILSON
C.G.I.A., C.Eng., F.I.E.E., F.I.E.R.E., M.B.I.M.

BERNARD BABANI (publishing) LTD
THE GRAMPIANS
SHEPHERDS BUSH ROAD
LONDON W6 7NF
ENGLAND

Although every care is taken with the preparation of this book, the publishers or author will not be responsible in any way for any errors that might occur.

First Published — September 1979

British Library Cataloguing in Publication Data
Wilson, F. A.
    Elements of electronics
    Book 2
    1. Electronic apparatus and appliances
    I. Title
    621. 381 TK7870

    ISBN 0 900162 83 X

Printed and Manufactued in Great Britain by C. Nicholls & Co. Ltd.

PREFACE

This is the second book in a series of three written especially as
a self-instructional course for those who either have had no
education in mathematics or perhaps have forgotten it all. The
course aims mainly at helping the reader to a serious understanding of the *elements* of electronics at low cost so that at the end
of Book 3 he or she will not only have covered sufficient
groundwork for a well balanced appreciation of many of the
more important basic electronics principles but also be able
to undertake more serious study of specialized electronics
subjects if desired, either from books which follow in this
series or from any other.

Where difficulty is likely to arise, additional emphasis is given
and with some repetition where it is necessary that important
features are emphasized.

This book is almost entirely concerned with Alternating
Current Theory, compared with Book 1 in which the reader is
introduced to the fascinating world of the electron and the
basic electronic circuit and with Book 3 which develops a
close acquaintance with the practical world of transistors and
their circuits. Book 2 may perhaps be considered a little less
exciting than its companions, yet it is of great importance,
because without some appreciation of the subject, the funda-
mentals of other branches of electronics will ever remain
obscure.

For the reader who may already have some knowledge of the simple electronic circuit, the first book is not essential for this present one has been written as a complete treatise and assumes no previous study of alternating currents whatsoever. Moreover it contains appendices covering all the additional mathematics required for circuit analysis. The appendices are usually indicated by a bracketed raised number, for example, "This is where the advantages of graphs [A2] become apparent" means that more information on graphs is contained in Appendix 2.

Unless the reader simply accepts the calculations given in the examples, he or she needs only to have and be able to use an inexpensive book of logarithmic tables, however if a calculator, especially a scientific one, is available, so much the better.

F. A. WILSON, C.G.I.A., C.Eng., F.I.E.E., F.I.E.R.E., M.B.I.M.

CONTENTS

1. ALTERNATING CURRENTS

In studies of direct currents polarity has always been recognizable within the circuit, that is, the e.m.f. (without which no electronic current flows) has its two terminals labelled + and −. The current is direct or *unidirectional*, it flows continuously in one direction only. The e.m.f. of an alternating current circuit on the other hand cannot be marked with polarity since it is continually changing over between + and −, resulting in the current reversing its direction similarly. In the electricity mains this takes place at 50 or 60 times in one second, in some communication circuits it is at a rate of thousands of millions of times in one second.

Much of the study material relies on graphs and also on a little trigonometry, the reader who has little acquaintance with either is therefore recommended to read Appendices 2 and 3 first, subsequently referring to them as necessary.

1.1 WAVEFORMS

Mention of the sea inevitably conjures up visions of waves, an ideal introduction to the main subject of this section for it is to electronic *waves*, fashioned in similar shape, that we owe our modern wonders of communication. This simplest form of wave demands our attention first so that subsequently with some knowledge of the vagaries of electrons and with a little more mathematics, we shall be able to examine in depth the *waveform* of any alternating current. It is only by analysis that we can understand how to generate and control electronic waves to do the fascinating things of which they are capable. Sound waves, radio waves, heat and light waves, perhaps even brain-waves are all based on the simple wave which is developed below.

1.1.1 Simple Harmonic Motion

Consider a guitar, piano or other musical string (hence the term *harmonic* motion) to be pulled from its rest position at O as in Fig. 1.1 (i) to position A. When released it quickly

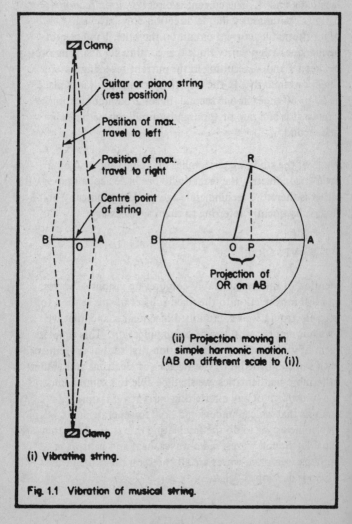

Clamp

Guitar or piano string
(rest position)

Position of max.
travel to left

Position of max.
travel to right

Centre point
of string

B   O   A

B   O   P   A

R

Projection of
OR on AB

(ii) Projection moving in
simple harmonic motion.
(AB on different scale to (i)).

Clamp

(i) Vibrating string.

Fig. 1.1 Vibration of musical string.

flies over to position B from which it returns to A. This whole movement then repeats and is the commencement of the ordinary vibratory motion which results in the pleasant sound wave which we hear. A point anywhere on the string actually moves according to a simple mathematical law. For simplicity consider the centre point O moving between A and B as drawn again in Fig. 1.1 (ii). A circle is constructed on the line AB as a diameter and a radius OR considered to rotate uniformly once round the circle in the time taken by the string to move from A to B and back to A again. Then the projection OP of OR on AB (obtained by drawing a line from R perpendicular to AB) describes the position of the string relative to point O and this projection moves in *simple harmonic motion* (s.h.m.). Let us take a practical example to make this clear, for example, for a middle-C piano wire which vibrates at 250 times per second.

Draw a line AB (Fig. 1.2) to represent the travel of the point O on the string. It will be seen as we progress that this type of diagram always starts at "3-o'clock" and rotation is anti-clockwise. Imagine the string which is clamped at some distance above and below the diagram, to be pulled to point A, then released. Our interest is in the position of the wire immediately after release so we mark the time of release $t = 0$.

Now if the string vibrates at 250 times per second, it must take $\dfrac{1}{250}$ secs for one complete vibration, i.e. $\dfrac{1000}{250} = 4.0$ ms.

Draw the circle with AB as diameter and centre O and let a radius rotate from the point at A anticlockwise round the circle to represent a time of 4.0 ms.

At 0.5 ms, OR will have completed $\dfrac{0.5}{4} = \dfrac{1}{8}$ of one revolution,

3

in degrees this is $\dfrac{360}{8} = 45°$, this is marked OR_1.

Draw a line perpendicular to AB from R_1 as shown, meeting AB at P_1. OP_1 is the projection of OR_1 on AB and P_1 gives the position of the centre point of the string 0.5 ms after release from A as shown dotted, travelling in the direction A to B.

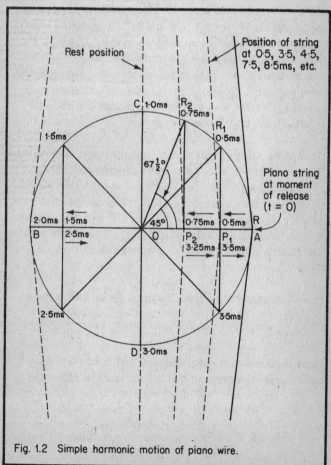

Fig. 1.2 Simple harmonic motion of piano wire.

4

Similarly P_2 is the position after 0.75 ms, O after 1.0 ms as shown. Any other position is similarly determined. At 2.0 ms the string reaches B and between 2 and 4 ms travels back to A. It is assumed that no forces such as air resistance are damping the vibration of the wire. When the wire returns to point A for the first time it is said to have completed one *wave* or *cycle*. It immediately commences the second cycle whereupon at OR_1 the rotating radius has turned through a total of 360° (one complete revolution) + 45° = 405° and R_1 is now labelled 4.5 ms.

Swings and pendulums are other examples of s.h.m. although at first acquaintance the description "simple" may appear to be doubt for clearly from Fig. 1.2 the distance the wire has travelled in the first 0.5 ms (represented by P_1 A) is very different from that in the second same period of time (OP_1). We shall need a little trigonometry to find the rules for this but first let us look at a "picture" of the waveform to get a clearer view of how the string position varies as time progresses. This is where the advantages of graphs[A2] become apparent.

In Fig. 1.2 it is shown that the projection of OR on AB moves in s.h.m. as the point R travels at a constant rate round the circle. The projection onto CD also moves in s.h.m. the only difference between the two being that when one is maximum the other is minimum although at an angle of 45° or one of its multiples both types of projection are equal. For a little extra convenience we use the vertical (CD) projection in Fig. 1.3 so that it can be projected directly to the right to determine the height of the curve for any time (or equally for any angle). The circumference of the circle is stretched out to form the straight line or X-axis[A2] and the graph of s.h.m. is plotted for the times (or angles) as shown. Wherever OR rests, its projection on CD is extended to the right to produce a point on the graph vertically above or below the appropriate time (or number of degrees) as marked on the scale, e.g. when

5

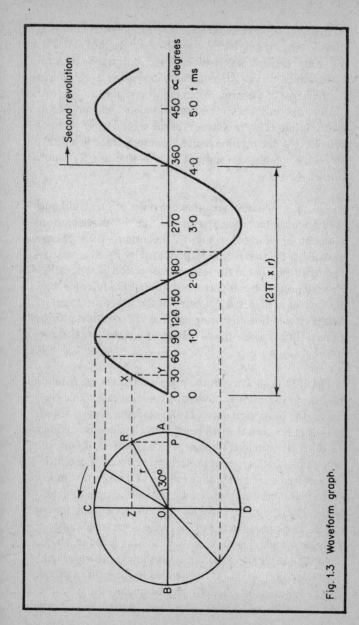

Fig. 1.3 Waveform graph.

the angle of rotation of OR from rest is 30° the point X is
obtained at the intersection of the horizontal line from R
with the vertical line from 30° (or 0.33 ms) on the scale.
By repeating this process for, say, every 15 or 30° the curve
is traced out.

Now the projection of OR on the axis CD is OZ and since RZ
and OP are parallel, then PR = OZ and from simple trigonometry[A3]

$$\sin 30° = \frac{PR}{OR} \qquad \therefore \ PR = OR \sin 30°$$

that is, XY, or the height of the waveform when OR has turned
through 30° is equal to the value of the length of the rotating
radius multiplied by the sine of the angle of its rotation. The
maximum height or value of the waveform is equal to OR,
therefore the value at any point is equal to the maximum value
multiplied by the sine of the angle through which it has moved
from the zero or rest position. Thus we call the waveform graph
of simple harmonic motion a *sine curve*, it is said to be
sinusoidal in shape. This fundamental waveform is very
important in electronics for simple alternating currents and
voltages are of this form. A good example is the electricity
supply mains which is described next because the method of
generation follows s.h.m. so closely.

1.1.2 The Alternating-Voltage Generator

The simplest mechanical alternating-voltage generator consists
of a single loop of wire which is rotated within a magnetic
field as shown in the sketch of Fig. 1.4. The mechanical
armature which holds the wires and rotates them is not
shown but the elementary current-collecting device is, that
is, two *slip rings*, S_1 and S_2 on which rub two fixed *carbon
brushes*. The slip-rings are insulated from each other and

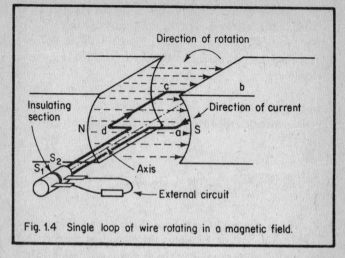

Fig. 1.4 Single loop of wire rotating in a magnetic field.

each is connected to one side of the loop. The brushes maintain good electrical contact with the rotating slip-rings and themselves are connected to the external circuit. For the direction of rotation shown the Left-Hand Rule gives an electronic current flow as indicated by the arrows, the sides of the loop ab and cd cutting the flux and producing induced e.m.f.'s in series-aiding (additive). The ends of the loop ad and bc move parallel to the flux and therefore do not cut it and generate an e.m.f. Larger e.m.f.'s are generated by increasing the number of turns on the coil.

To predict the type of waveform this gnerator produces, we might simply imagine the magnetic flux to be concentrated in lines and use those of graph paper to save drawing our own. This has been done in Fig. 1.5 (i) which shows the path traced out by one side of the loop in moving from the bottom (270°) to the top (90°) position. We are looking into the wire itself which is shown at 270°. At this point the wire is moving parallel to the horizontal flux lines and no e.m.f. is generated. In the next, say, 10° of movement (to 280°), the wire has risen on the graph through 1.5 lines, in the

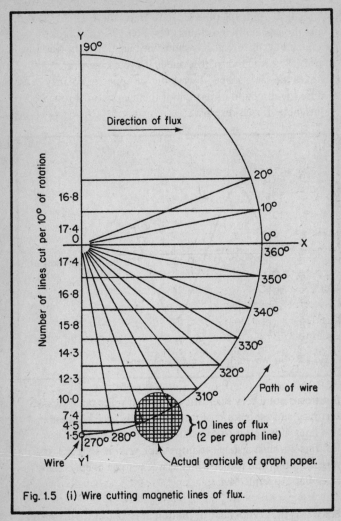

Fig. 1.5 (i) Wire cutting magnetic lines of flux.

next 10° through 4.5 and then through 7, ultimately to a maximum of 17.4 (350–360° and 0–10°). These amounts may be read off the YY′ axis. Because the velocity of the wire is constant, each number represents the lines cut in a given period of time and hence is a measure of the e.m.f.

9

generated. By plotting on a separate graph these values against the mean wire positions over each $10°$, the shape of the e.m.f. wave is revealed as shown in Fig. 1.5(ii). In travelling from $270°$ through 0 to $90°$, one half-cycle is generated, $90-270°$ produces the same shape of wave but of opposite polarity because the direction of motion of the conductor through the magnetic flux is reversed.

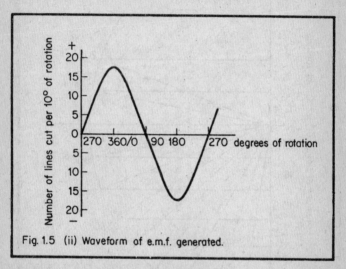

Fig. 1.5 (ii) Waveform of e.m.f. generated.

But this is not a very scientific method, it relies on drawing accuracy and estimation of fractions of distance between two lines, it is better to calculate using trigonometry. For this we must also get to grips with *vectors* so it is suggested that the reader who has not yet met them, should next read Appendix 4.1.

Since it is the component of motion at rt.∠s to the flux lines which generates the e.m.f., we first resolve the circular motion of the wire at any given instant to find this component, that is, whatever the direction in which the wire is travelling, just how fast does it move directly across the flux? Fig. 1.6 shows how this is done when the wire at R is travelling in a circular path, the radius OR being at an angle ϕ (Greek, phi) to some reference point, in this case the OY' axis as used in Fig. 1.5.

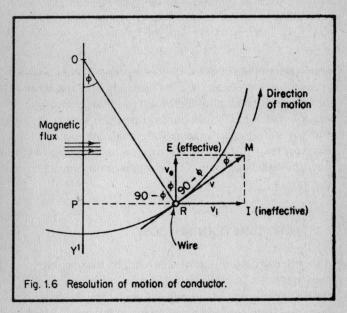

Fig. 1.6 Resolution of motion of conductor.

A tangent to the circle (a straight-line touching, but not cutting the circle) is drawn at point R. This is labelled RM and can be shown to be at rt.∠s to the radius OR at the point of contact. RM is marked off to a convenient length to represent the velocity of the conductor, it thus becomes a vector. It is resolved into two components at rt.∠s RE and RI by completing the rectangle REMI. RE is at rt.∠s to the flux and therefore is effective in producing an e.m.f., RI is parallel to the flux and thus is ineffective. Since RM represents the velocity of the conductor, then RE and RI are both vectors together equivalent to RM and representing the "effective" and "ineffective" components v_e and v_i respectively.

Let RP be drawn perpendicular to OY', then $\angle$ORP = $(90-\phi)°$

11

and because $\angle PRE = 90°$, $\angle ORE = \phi$. Similarly, because $\angle ORM = 90°$, then $\angle ERM = (90-\phi)°$ and $\angle RME = \phi$. Then, considering the rt.$\angle$d triangle REM,

$$\frac{ER}{RM} = \sin\phi \quad \therefore ER = RM \sin\phi$$

or in terms of the velocities: $v_e = v\sin\phi$, that is, the effective velocity which produces the e.m.f. is equal to the actual conductor velocity multiplied by the sine of the angle through which its radius has turned, proving that a sine-wave is generated. Sine waves are not just a theoretical consideration, public supply mains are mostly sinusoidal as are the outputs of many transistor *oscillators* which generate the waves needed for communication purposes.

1.2 WAVEFORM TERMINOLOGY

Although most theoretical work is based on the sine wave, we must appreciate from the start that many other waveshapes exist, even square and triangular and graphs may be drawn of them. On the other hand waves produced by speech change so rapidly and are so complex that analysis by standard techniques is not feasible. This section therefore explains the terms used for repetitive waveforms only, that is, those which present a certain shape or form within a given time period, continually repeating this form thereafter.

1.2.1 The Cycle

Referring to any waveform graph as for example Fig. 1.3, a *cycle* is defined as that part of a wave between two successive points having the same value and at which the wave is varying in the same direction. Thus in Fig. 1.3 one cycle is completed between 0 and 360°, between 30 and 390°, 31 and 391° etc. In

each case the two successive points have the same value and
the wave is rising. For one cycle the rotating radius OR moves
through a complete circle, irrespective of its starting point.

1.2.2 Period

The time taken for one complete cycle is called the *period*
of the waveform. The *periodic time* is usually denoted by T.

1.2.3 Angular Measure

The concept of a sine wave derived from a rotating radius which
completes one revolution per cycle is very useful because most
analysis is concerned with one, or at the most, a few cycles
at a time. The time taken for one cycle however can vary from
nanoseconds (10^{-9} secs) to seconds so to avoid the complication of differing time scales it is sometimes more convenient
to work to a scale of degrees with $360°$ per revolution or
cycle. But we must never lose sight of the fact that what we
are basically concerned with is time, working in angles is just a
useful simplification.

1.2.4 Radian Measure

Fig. 1.5 is a practical demonstration of a rotating vector for it
shows how an e.m.f. is generated when a conductor traces
out a circular path within a magnetic field, the conductor is
then said to have a *linear velocity*. The rotating vector which
may represent the e.m.f. generated in the conductor is also
seen to have an *angular velocity*, that is, it moves through so
many degrees per second.

Since the e.m.f. generated is a function of the linear velocity it
is frequently useful to have an angular measure which bears a
relationship to the linear travel and the *radian* (rad.) is such
a unit. It is the angle through which the vector has moved when

its point has traversed a distance equal to its own length, that is, a length equal to the radius, see Fig. 1.7. If the radius is denoted by r

$$OR = OR_1 = RR_1 = r$$

and since the circumference of the circle = $2\pi r$, there are $\dfrac{2\pi r}{r} = 2\pi$ radians in a circle.

In degrees therefore, 1 radian = $\dfrac{360}{2\pi}$ = 57.296°, usually shown as 57.3°

Thus, commensurate with linear velocity of a conductor, we have angular velocity of the rotating vector and this is most conveniently expressed for electronic work in radians per second (rads/s). It is denoted by the Greek letter ω (omega) and instead of labelling the X-axes of our graphs 0−360° for one cycle we shall sometimes find the scale 0−2π radians more convenient. Note however, that this scale also takes no account of time, it is only useful when we are interested in the *shape* of the wave.

1.2.5 Frequency

The *frequency* of a wave is the number of cycles completed per second. It is denoted by f and 1 cycle per second is known as 1 Hertz (Hz, after Heinrich Hertz, a German physicist).

Earlier we discussed a string vibrating at 250 times in 1 second, the string produces *sound waves* in the air (at 250 Hz) which we hear. Good hearing extends over a range from about 20 to 16,000 (16 kHz) or even higher but most people have a range less than this. We call this the *audio* (Latin, hear) range, the lower frequencies are the *bass* and the higher ones the *treble*. Within this range come the mains

14

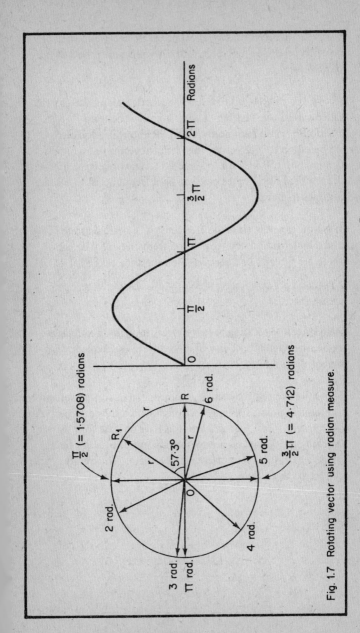

Fig. 1.7 Rotating vector using radian measure.

power frequencies mostly at 50 or 60 Hz and when they are made to produce an audible sound we recognize the low note of *mains hum.*

Above 16—20 kHz up to a few megahertz, sound waves exist called *supersonic* (Latin — above sound — the term *ultrasonic* is also commonly used). Radio transmissions are based on *carrier* waves, the frequency range of which is from about 150 kHz up to some 20 GHz, while transmission over optical fibres takes place at light frequencies, thousands of times higher.

It is now possible to relate frequency (f), periodic time (T) and angular frequency (ω). For a frequency of f Hz, since there are f cycles in 1 second, then the time taken for 1 cycle must be $\dfrac{1}{f}$ seconds, i.e. $T = \dfrac{1}{f}$ and $f = \dfrac{1}{T}$.

Also since the rotating vector moves through 2π radians per cycle, the angular velocity of a waveform of frequency f is $2\pi \times f$, i.e. $\omega = 2\pi f$.

If t is the elapsed time since commencement of a waveform from a reference point, the angle through which the rotating vector has turned is $2\pi ft$, i.e. ωt. We thus have at least four ways of labelling the X-axis on a waveform graph, the choice being made according to the particular problem. The quarter cycle points are as follows:

0	90	180	270	360	degrees
0	$\dfrac{\pi}{2}$	π	$\dfrac{3\pi}{2}$	2π	radians
0	$\dfrac{T}{4}$	$\dfrac{T}{2}$	$\dfrac{3T}{4}$	T	seconds
0	$\dfrac{\pi}{2\omega}$	$\dfrac{\pi}{\omega}$	$\dfrac{3\pi}{2\omega}$	$\dfrac{2\pi}{\omega}$	seconds

All very confusing perhaps when first met but confusion gets less with practice.

EXAMPLE:
The power mains frequency is 50 Hz. What is (i) the period, (ii) the angular velocity in degrees/sec and radians/sec, (iii) the angular movement in 10 ms?

(i) Period, $T = \dfrac{1}{f} = \dfrac{1}{50} = \underline{0.02 \text{ s.}}$

(ii) Angular velocity $= 360 \times f = 360 \times 50 = $
$$\underline{18,000 \text{ degrees/s.}}$$
Angular velocity $= 2\pi \times f = 100\pi = \underline{314.2 \text{ rad/s.}}$

(iii) Angular movement in 10 ms $= 2\pi \text{ ft} =$
$$2\pi \times 50 \times \frac{10}{1000} = \underline{\pi \text{ radians}} \ (180°).$$

1.2.6 Wavelength

Sound and radio waves travel over distances through the air or space, electric waves also travel by wire, tube or fibre, in each case the journey is made at a certain known velocity. We can therefore ascribe to any particular frequency the length of the path travelled by the wave during one cycle, that is, during periodic time. This is known as the *wavelength* which is denoted by λ (Greek, lambda). Now, from the simple relationship:

distance $=$ average velocity $\times$ time, we have

$\lambda = $ velocity (v) $\times T$ and since $T = \dfrac{1}{f}$

$\lambda = \dfrac{\text{velocity}}{\text{frequency}} = \dfrac{v}{f}.$

For radio transmissions the velocity of the wave is the same as that of light (usually designated by c) and is very slightly less than 3×10^8 m/s (3×10^{10} cm/s) and these are the values we use with negligible loss of accuracy. This velocity is unbelievably high, in fact sufficiently so that radio communication from one end of the Earth to the other suffers no noticeable delay. However, with communication via a satellite where the latter is some 36,000 km above the Earth, delays are just appreciable. To the Moon we are beginning to experience difficulties as the following example shows.

EXAMPLE:
What is the transmission delay from the Moon which is approximately 385,000 km away?

$$\text{Transmission time} = \frac{\text{distance}}{\text{velocity}} = \frac{385{,}000 \times 10^3 \text{ m}}{3 \times 10^8 \text{ m/s}} = \underline{1.283 \text{ secs}}$$

(a free and easy telephone conversation is not possible with such a delay both ways).

EXAMPLE:
The medium waveband of a radio receiver is marked from 500 to 1,600 kHz. What is the equivalent wavelength range?

$$v \text{ for radio waves} = 3 \times 10^8 \text{ m/s} \quad f = 500 \times 10^3 \text{ Hz}$$

$$\therefore \lambda = \frac{v}{f} = \frac{3 \times 10^8}{500 \times 10^3} = \frac{3 \times 10^3}{5} = \underline{600 \text{ m.}}$$

When f = 16,000 kHz

$$\lambda = \frac{3 \times 10^8}{1600 \times 10^3} = \frac{3 \times 10^3}{16} = \underline{187.5 \text{ m.}}$$

$\therefore$ Equivalent wavelength range is $\underline{600-187.5 \text{ m.}}$ (note that as frequency goes up, wavelength goes down).

EXAMPLE:
A quarter-wavelength aerial is required to work at 60 MHz.
What length should it be?

$$\lambda \text{ at } 60 \text{ MHz} = \frac{v}{f} = \frac{3 \times 10^8}{60 \times 10^6} = 5 \text{ m.}$$

$\therefore$ Length of aerial $= \frac{1}{4} \times$ wavelength $= \frac{5}{4} = \underline{1.25 \text{ m.}}$

EXAMPLE:
A burglar alarm emits supersonic waves at 40 kHz. What is
the wavelength? (Velocity of waves in air is approx. 340 m/s.)

$$\lambda = \frac{v}{f} = \frac{340}{40 \times 10^3} = 0.0085 \text{ m} = \underline{0.85 \text{ cm.}}$$

(Note: v has a very different value for audio and supersonic
waves compared with radio waves).

1.2.7 Phase

This is a term which will frequently arise in our future delibera-
tions so we must be certain of understanding what it actually
means. One of the dictionary definitions is appropriate, "a
particular stage in a recurring sequence of movements or
changes". Consider again the rotating vector of Fig. 1.3.
The "recurring sequence" is the continuation of complete
revolutions or cycles of the waveform. "Particular stage"
means any part of the circle or cycle. So far we have consistently considered the vector and waveform as commencing
at the reference point (3 o'clock on the circle, marked 0
degrees, radians or time). This is one particular stage but
clearly any other point is also. When the vector is at
another point, its angle relative to the reference is known
as the *phase angle*. Phase angle has most significance
when we consider two or more waves acting together

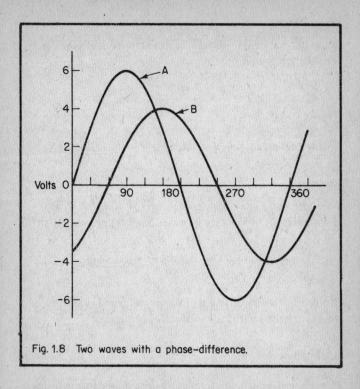

Fig. 1.8 Two waves with a phase–difference.

in the same circuit, for example, as shown in Fig. 1.8 where
two waves of the same frequency (and therefore, period)
exist with a *phase difference* of 60° (1.047 radians).
Wave B has a phase angle relative to A of 60°, that is,
B reaches any particular stage (say, zero or maximum)
when the waves have turned through a further 60°. Knowing
the frequency, we can calculate the actual time delay from

$$t = \frac{\text{phase angle in degrees}}{360\,f} \quad \text{or} \quad t = \frac{\text{phase angle in radians}}{\omega}.$$

Thus from the figure, if the waveform illustrates a
frequency of 50 Hz, the time delay for B is

$$\frac{60}{360 \times 50} = 0.0033 \text{ secs} = 3.3 \text{ ms} \text{ using the first formula}$$

and $\dfrac{1.047}{2\pi \times 50}$ = 3.3 ms using the second.

In the figure, B is said to be *lagging* on A by 60° or
equally A is *leading* B by 60°. (Quite correctly, B is
leading on the second cycle of A by 300° — a complication
in which we need not become involved at present.)

A constant phase difference can only apply when A and B
have the same frequency, for if they have not, the relative
phase continually changes. Fig. 1.8 also shows that the
waveforms A and B may have different *amplitudes*, that
is their maximum values are different. Amplitude in no way
affects phase difference.

It will be seen from Fig. A 3.5 in Appendix 3 that the cosine
wave can be said to lead the sine wave by 90°. The two waves
are 90° $\left(\dfrac{\pi}{2} \text{ radians} \right)$ *out of phase.*

Phasors: Appendix 4 also introduces the concept of the
phasor as a special application of vectors, representing
magnitude and phase instead of magnitude and direction, we
therefore adopt the new term when rotating vectors and
phase angles are concerned. The phasors for the waveforms
of Fig. 1.8 are as shown in Fig. 1.9 (i). Two concentric circles
are necessary because the waveforms have different amplitudes, hence phasors of different lengths. We find that the
circles and even the graphs can often be dispensed with,
leaving only the phasors because they completely specify
the two sinusoidal waveforms and their positions relative to
each other. Put in a slightly different way, the simple phasor
diagram of Fig. 1.9 (ii) is all we need to be able to draw the
complete waveform graph of Fig. 1.8. Recalling that the

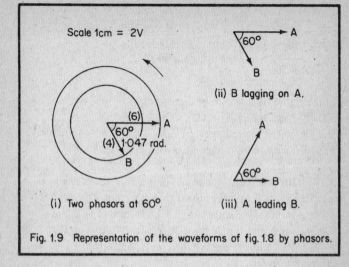

Fig. 1.9 Representation of the waveforms of fig. 1.8 by phasors.

direction of rotation of the phasors is anti-clockwise (ii) shows B lagging on the reference phasor A by 60°. In (iii) the reference phasor is B with A leading by 60°. When one phasor represents current in a circuit and another phasor represents voltage, separate scales are necessary which should be quoted.

1.3 THE SPECIAL CHARACTERISTICS OF THE SINE WAVE

Although sinusoidal waves are mentioned frequently in the previous section, most of it refers to repetitive waves generally rather than to sine waves exclusively. Some waves other than sinusoidal we shall meet later but it is already evident that since sinusoidal waves can be represented by single phasors and it can be shown by a phasor diagram how two or more of them may exist in a circuit together even though in different phases, we have a powerful tool for analysis of complex circuits. Also although a practical circuit may carry waves

22

other than sinusoidal, we can still use the latter for investigation and understanding. This section now looks more closely
at features exclusive to the sine wave itself.

1.3.1 The General Equation

The conclusion reached earlier and which Fig. 1.3 illustrates is
that the value of a waveform at any point is equal to the
length of the phasor multiplied by the sine of the angle which
it makes with the reference axis, that is, OR sin ϕ. OR represents in the practical circuit the *peak* (maximum) value
of the sinusoidal quantity (voltage or current), thus for OR we
may substitute E_m or I_m for the maximum values, letting e
and i represent the *instantaneous* values. The general sine
wave equations are therefore

$$e = E_m \sin (360 \text{ ft})° \quad \text{or} \quad e = E_m \sin \omega t \text{ (radians, } \omega = 2\pi f)$$

$$i = I_m \sin (360 \text{ ft})° \quad \text{or} \quad i = I_m \sin \omega t \text{ (radians, } \omega = 2\pi f)$$

according to whether we are working in degrees or radians. These
equations refer to the reference axis but as Fig. 1.9 shows,
when, for example, A and B are both rotating at the same angular
velocity with a constant phase difference between them, we may
need an additional component in the equation for the non-
reference quantity, that is

$$e = E_m \sin (\omega t + \phi)$$

$$i = I_m \sin (\omega t + \phi) \text{ when the angle is expressed in}$$

radians.

Thus in Fig. 1.9 (iii) the angle ϕ for phasor A is zero, for B
it is -1.047 (note the minus sign when the phasor is lagging)
and the general equation for the voltage waveform represented
by phasor A for which the maximum value is 6 volts and the
frequency is 50 Hz is

$$e = 6 \sin(100\pi t)$$

and for the waveform represented by phasor B

$$e = 4 \sin(100\pi t - 1.047)$$

so that for any given value of t in seconds the actual voltage of the waves at that instant can be calculated. One example only follows because we shall seldom need calculations in terms of time but more with regard to phase differences and then fortunately these will be found to be mostly at 90°.

EXAMPLE:
A waveform (A) is expressed by $e = E_m \sin \omega t$. The frequency is 200 kHz and the maximum value, E_m, is 10V. What is the instantaneous voltage after 1 microsecond and what is it for a second waveform similar but lagging by an angle of $\frac{\pi}{2}$ radians?

$$E_m = 10V \quad f = 200 \times 10^3 \text{ Hz} \quad \omega = 2\pi f = 4\pi \times 10^5 \text{ rads/s.}$$
$$t = 1 \times 10^{-6} \text{ s.}$$

Then $e = E_m \sin \omega t$

$$= 10 \sin(4\pi \times 10^5 \times 10^{-6}) = 10 \sin(0.4\pi)$$

$$= 10 \sin 1.2566$$

We now need the sine of 1.2566 radians. Some books of tables include one especially for this, others have a "degree to radians" table. Calculation is quite easy however, for radians are changed to degrees by multiplying by $\frac{360}{2\pi}$ $\left(\text{i.e. } \frac{180}{\pi}\right)$.

Go back one step to 0.4π instead of 1.2566 and

$$0.4\pi \text{ radians} = 0.4\pi \times \frac{180}{\pi} \text{ degrees} = 0.4 \times 180 = 72°$$

and $\sin 72° = 0.9511$

$$\therefore e = 10 \times 0.9511 = \underline{9.511 \text{ volts}}.$$

which could also be obtained, but with less accuracy, by drawing the waveform to a maximum height on the scale representing 10V and measuring the height of the curve at 0.4π radians. This is shown in Fig. 1.10 for wave A.

For the second waveform, B, E_m, f, ω and t are the same, only the phase angle is different, then

$$e = E_m \sin(\omega t + \phi) \qquad \phi = -\frac{\pi}{2} \text{ (minus because the phasor is lagging)}$$

$$= 10 \sin\left(0.4\pi - \frac{\pi}{2}\right)$$

$$= 10 \sin(-0.1\pi) = 10 \sin\left(-0.1\pi \times \frac{180}{\pi}\right)°$$

$$= 10 \sin(-18)°$$

$$= 10 \sin(360 - 18)° = 10 \sin 342°.$$

In Appendix 3 we are reminded that for angles greater than 90° and in the 4th Quadrant we use $(360° - \theta)$, i.e. $360° - 342 = 18°$, and that sine is negative.

$$\therefore e = 10 \times -(\sin 18°) = 10 \times -0.3090 = \underline{-3.09 \text{ volts}}$$

again, shown in Fig. 1.10. This figure helps to demonstrate the important point that after any time interval the two waves, being of the same frequency, have the same phase relationship to each other, they can be imagined as being locked together and rotating at ω rads/sec. Also since the net voltage at any given time is the algebraic sum of the individual wave voltages,

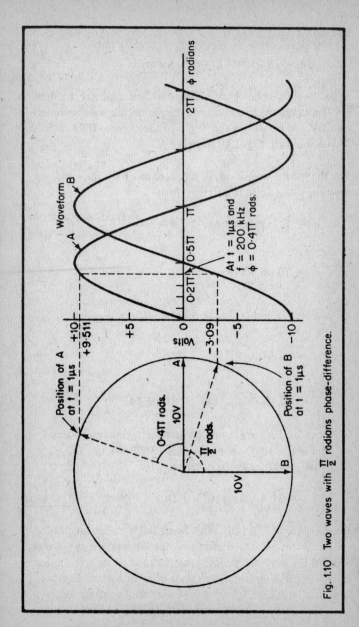

Fig. 1.10 Two waves with $\frac{\pi}{2}$ radians phase-difference.

26

the effective voltage of the two waves together at, say,
t = 1 μs is +9.511 − 3.09 = 6.421V. If a graph of the algebraic
sum of the two voltages is plotted for times or angles extending
over one cycle, it will be found to be sinusoidal and differing in
phase from both the component waves. As already mentioned,
we need not plot the graph, all the information usually required is
given by the phasors.

1.3.2 Peak and Average Values

A term defining the magnitude of a waveform has already
been introduced in the general equation, that is, the peak or
maximum value, E_m or I_m. The wave only reaches this
value twice per cycle (once positive, once negative) but
apart from being part of the general equation, it is useful
for comparison of waves and in practical work although
the wave spends most of its time away from the peak value,
it is this value which, for example, determines insulation
requirements.

A second characteristic describing a sine wave is the *average*
value, the simple arithmetical average of all the instantaneous values (the average of a set of figures is obtained by
finding their total and dividing by the number of figures).
We need only consider one half-cycle as all are the same
shape and in fact, because each quarter-cycle is produced
from the same set of numbers (sine values from 0−90°),
we can do all the calculations we need from the quarter-
cycle as long as we remember that the maximum value
(1.0) is shared equally between two quarter-cycles.

The calculation is made by adding all the sine values (e.g.
from Table A3.1)[A3] from 0 to 90° at small intervals,
say, every 5°, but allowing a value of 0.5 for 90°. The
total (11.45188) when divided by the number of values
18) gives an average of 0.6362. Mathematically the

27

value can be shown to be $\frac{2}{\pi}$ (0.6366), the inaccuracy lying in the first method for theoretically an infinte number [A4.4] of points should be taken, so

Average value of sinusoidal wave,

$$E_{av} = \frac{2}{\pi} \times E_m = 0.637 \, E_m$$

and $\quad I_{av} = \frac{2}{\pi} \times I_m = 0.637 \, I_m$.

1.3.3 Effective or Root-Mean-Square Value

Power in a dc circuit is simply calculated from $I^2 R$ or $\frac{E^2}{R}$ where I and E are current and voltage and R is the circuit resistance. As soon as we want to find the power in an ac circuit we realise the difficulty in that I and E are not constant. The maximum values are clearly not appropriate for the wave has a value nearly always less than the maximum. We have just found a multiplying factor (0.637) to convert I_{max} to I_{av} and now we need similarly to find one to convert I_{max} (or E_{max}) to I, the *effective value* so that a certain value of I in the ac case dissipates the same power in a resistive circuit as the same value of I in the dc case. The point about a "resistive" circuit is made because later it will be seen that circuits other than purely resistive, i.e. having a phase difference between current and voltage, are not quite so straightforward.

As an example, the public supply mains are quoted in this way. Although alternating at 50 or 60 Hz, a 200V ac supply will provide the same power on average in say, an electric fire as a 200V dc supply. We have to say "on average" because the ac power is obviously not constant throughout each cycle. It would seem that the 200V ac mains has a maximum value above 200V and this is so but it is now easy to see why 200V is called the "effective" value.

The general equation for a sine wave current tells us that the instantaneous value

$$i = I_m \sin \omega t,$$

and if we wish to calculate the power, p, at any instant,

$$p = i^2 R \;=\; (I_m \sin \omega t)^2 R \;=\; I_m^2 R (\sin \omega t)^2$$

$(\sin \omega t)^2$ is usually written $\sin^2 \omega t$ so

$$p = I_m^2 R \sin^2 \omega t .$$

$I_m^2 R$ is constant, so we can see how the power varies by drawing the graph of $\sin^2 \omega t$, the wave with which we are now conversant, but with each value squared. This is given in Fig.1.11 which firstly shows that the power is *pulsating* at twice the frequency of the wave producing it and also demonstrates that power is equally produced for positive and negative half-cycles, the square of a negative quantity being positive. This latter point makes sense from our knowledge of the production of heat in in a resistance, it obviously does not matter in which direction electrons are flowing for collisions to occur with atoms.

Finding the average power over one cycle needs no mathematics for it can be seen from Fig.1.11 that a line drawn at $P_m/2$ as shown dotted cuts the wave into two equal parts, for each cycle there is a total of two half-waves above the line and two below thus

$$P_{av} = \frac{P_m}{2} \quad \text{or, in words, the average power in a resistive}$$

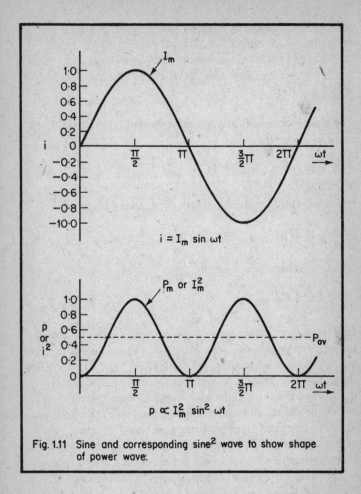

Fig. 1.11 Sine and corresponding sine² wave to show shape of power wave.

circuit when the current is a sine-wave is equal to one-half the peak power.

Now the maximum power is equal to (max. current)² x R i.e.
$P_m = I_m^2 R$

$$\therefore P_{av} = \frac{P_m}{2} = \frac{I_m^2 R}{2}$$

and recalling that we are finding the effective values of current or voltage, P (in the dc case) = P_{av} (in the ac case) = I^2R

$$\therefore I^2R = \frac{I_m^2 R}{2} \quad \text{(divide both sides by R and take square root)}$$

$$\therefore I = \frac{I_m}{\sqrt{2}} = 0.707\ I_m$$

also $I_m = \sqrt{2}I$. Similarly $E = 0.707\ E_m$ and $E_m = \sqrt{2}E$, thus if I is the value of direct current producing a certain power in a given resistance R, then a sine-wave of maximum value $\sqrt{2}I$ will do the same, irrespective of frequency.

From Fig.1.11 since the line representing P_{av} is the average or *mean* of the values of i *squared* and we have taken the square *root* of this to find the effective value, the latter is also known as the *Root-Mean-Square* value (rms) and although a more awkward term than "effective" it is precise and is the one in general use. Unless otherwise stated, E and I stand for rms values. It will be noticed that the rms value occurs at 45° ($\pi/4$ rads), since sin 45° = 0.707.

EXAMPLE:
What is the general equation for a 120V 60Hz mains supply?

$$e = E_m \sin \omega t \quad E_m = \sqrt{2}E = \sqrt{2} \times 120 = 169.7V$$

$$\omega = 2\pi f = 2\pi \times 60 = 377\ \text{rads/s.}$$

$$\therefore \underline{e = 169.7 \sin 377t \text{ volts.}}$$

EXAMPLE:
A 100 watt lamp when working on ac mains has a resistance of 400 ohms. What is the peak voltage across it?

$$P = 100W \quad R = 400\Omega$$

$$P = \frac{E^2}{R} \quad \therefore \ E = \sqrt{RP} = \sqrt{400 \times 100} = 200V,$$

this is the rms supply value. Then $E_m = \sqrt{2}E =$
$\sqrt{2} \times 200 = 282.8V.$

1.3.4 Analysis Methods

The example in Sect.1.3.1 led to the idea that when two or
more sine waves of the same frequency act together in a
circuit, the resultant could be obtained from the graphs
by adding corresponding instantaneous values of voltage
or of current together over the whole cycle (this does not
apply to a mixture of voltage and current waves since these
can never be added). This is a tedious process and we have
already touched on the use of phasors when getting to grips
with phase itself in Sect.1.2.7. In a phasor diagram the
components are considered to rotate at the same frequency,
hence because two or more waves of the same frequency
add to produce a resultant at that frequency the phasor
diagram has much to offer. Proof of this is obtained
graphically as Fig.1.10 shows.

Just as a reminder, Fig.1.10 also demonstrates how we can
conveniently represent a sinusoidal waveform by a rotating
phasor and waves of the same frequency but not moving
in time with each other result in phasors rotating together
but separated by the angle which is equivalent to the time
difference. Thus we solve the difficulty of representing
time by changing it to an angle which is much more easily
manipulated by both diagram and mathematics.

To distinguish between phasors representing current and
those representing voltage, a closed arrow head is used for
current and an open one for voltage thus

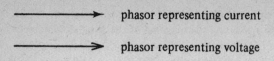

→ phasor representing current

→ phasor representing voltage

Addition of Phasors:

If the addition of two waves of the same frequency results in a third wave at that frequency, there must be a single phasor to represent this wave. Although we shall be dealing mainly with finding the resultant of two waves 90° apart, the general method for the addition of phasors is developed first.

Consider two phasors OA and OB as in Fig.1.12 (i), with A leading B by an angle ϕ. If the lengths of the phasors represent say, maximum currents I_a and I_b then the general equations are:

$$I_a \sin(\omega t + \phi) \text{ and } I_b \sin \omega t.$$

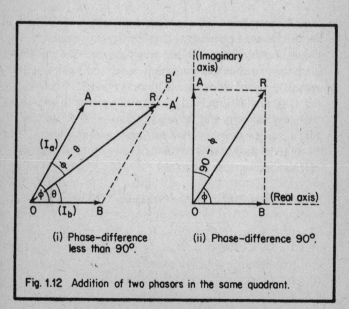

(i) Phase-difference less than 90°.

(ii) Phase-difference 90°.

Fig. 1.12 Addition of two phasors in the same quadrant.

It can be shown that the phasor representing the sum of the two waves is given by the diagonal of the parallelogram[A5] set up with OA and OB as adjacent sides. The diagonal OR is the resultant phasor, leading OB by an angle θ and therefore lagging on OA by $(\phi - \theta)$. OR and the angles it makes with the other phasors can be obtained with ruler and protractor, equally it may be calculated as is shown later. Even when we calculate, it is often advantageous to draw the phasor diagram, approximately to scale as a check on calculations.

Considering smaller and smaller values of ϕ and carrying out the same construction shows that at $\phi = 0$, the magnitude of the resultant phasor is equal to the sum of the magnitudes of the components and it is in phase with them. Similarly as ϕ reaches $180°$ the resultant phasor becomes equal to the difference between the two components and is in phase with the greater one.

Most frequently we will need to add two phasors at rt$\angle$s for this, as will be developed later is what happens in circuits containing capacitance or inductance. The parallelogram then takes on the more easily constructed shape of a rectangle, the resultant phasor forming two rt$\angle$d triangles e.g. OAR and OBR in Fig.1.12 (ii) which can be solved using trigonometry and Pythagoras' Theorem[A3]. In this case a constructional method and measurement is less likely to be used in view of the simplicity of the alternative, calculation, for since BR = OA

$$OR^2 = OA^2 + OB^2 \quad \text{(Pythagoras' Theorem)}$$

$$\therefore OR = \sqrt{OA^2 + OB^2}$$

$$\text{and} \tan \phi = \frac{OA}{OB} \quad \therefore \phi = \tan^{-1} \frac{OA}{OB}$$

giving both the magnitude and phase relationship of the resultant phasor, OR

Also $\dfrac{OB}{OR}$ = cos ϕ ∴ OB = OR cos ϕ

and $\dfrac{OA}{OR}$ = cos $(90° - \phi)$ = sin ϕ ∴ OA = OR sin ϕ.

so that given a phasor OR $\angle \phi$, it can be resolved into two component phasors at rt $\angle$s, usually one along the reference axis (e.g. OB) and one at rt $\angle$s to the reference axis (e.g. OA). The component along the reference axis is called the *real* component, the other the *imaginary* component, a term which can be misleading as it is seemingly just as real as the first, but it is a mathematical term and its meaning will be better appreciated when we study complex numbers. Also when two phasors are separated by $90°$ they are said to be in *quadrature*.

Describing a phasor such as OR by its magnitude and phase angle is expressing it in *polar coordinates* (polar-relating to a fixed point known as a "pole", in this case the centre of a circle), the length only of the phasor is known as the *modulus* (Latin, measure) and this is specially shown by enclosing the symbol within vertical lines, e.g. |E| or |I|, frequently done when we are not considering the angle yet are recognizing that there is one. The angle itself is sometimes known as the *argument* (an early English mathematical term for an angle on which the calculation of another quantity depends — we will however use the term "phase angle" or sometimes just "angle" to avoid unnecessary confusion with terms). OA and OB are known as the *rectangular coordinates*.

The following example is designed to illustrate the use of the principles so far outlined:

EXAMPLE:

Two sinusoidal voltages of the same frequency act together
in a circuit, E_1 is 20V and leads the current in the circuit
by 70°, E_2 is 15V and lags on the current by 130°. What
is the sum of the two voltages?

Firstly we can obtain the answer graphically with ruler,
protractor and set square. The (horizontal) reference phasor
OI is first drawn to a convenient length to represent the
current (Fig.1.13 — suggested scales are given on diagrams
where appropriate) and from point O, phasor OE_1 is drawn at
70° to OI and 20 units long according to the scale chosen.
Similarly OE_2 is drawn at 130° clockwise from OI (the
voltage *lags* on the current) and 15 units long. We now
have to find the resultant of OE_1 and OE_2.

Draw a line from E_2 parallel[A5] to OE_1 and one from E_1
parallel to OE_2 (shown dotted in the figure). Mark the
point where these two lines cross, R. Then $OE_1 RE_2$ is
a parallelogram and OR is the resultant phasor. Its length
and angle with OI are then measured, the length being
converted to volts, giving approximately 7.8V ∠111°.

By calculation, we first resolve both OE_1 and OE_2 into
their real and imaginary (horizontal and vertical) components, then because the two real components are acting
along the same line they can be added together (with due
regard to direction), similarly with the imaginary components thus:

Rectangular coordinates of OE_1,

real $= 20 \cos 70° = 20 \times 0.3420 = 6.84$
imag. $= 20 \sin 70° = 20 \times 0.9397 = 18.79$

(both positive, see Figs. A3.3 and A3.4 in Appendix 3).

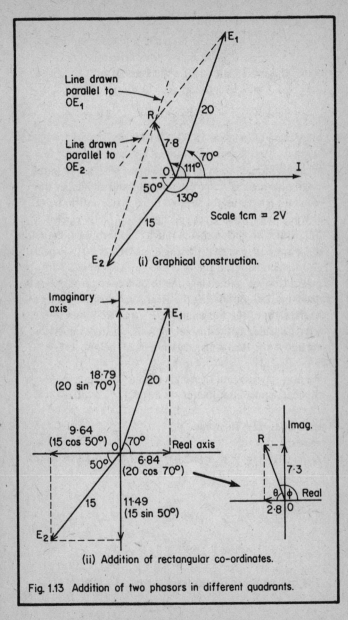

Line drawn parallel to OE₁

R

Line drawn parallel to OE₂

7·8

20

70°

111°

O

50°

130°

I

15

Scale 1cm = 2V

E₂

(i) Graphical construction.

Imaginary axis

E₁

18·79
(20 sin 70°)

20

9·64
(15 cos 50°)

O

70°

Real axis

50°

6·84
(20 cos 70°)

15

11·49
(15 sin 50°)

E₂

Imag.

R

7·3

θ   φ

Real

2·8   O

(ii) Addition of rectangular co-ordinates.

Fig. 1.13 Addition of two phasors in different quadrants.

37

Rectangular coordinates of OE_2,

$$\text{real} = 15 \cos -130° = 15 \cos 230° = -15 \cos 50°$$
$$= -15 \times 0.6428 = -9.64$$

$$\text{imag.} = 15 \sin -130° = 15 \sin 50°$$
$$= -15 \times 0.766 = -11.49$$

Sum of real $= 6.84 - 9.64 = -2.8$V

Sum of imag. $= 18.79 - 11.49 = 7.3$V.

What we have done so far is shown in Fig. 1.13(ii) and clearly having a sketch of the phasors and an idea of the resultant is very useful because it helps to confirm that any juggling with degrees and signs is correctly carried out. But with such a sketch much is seen through common-sense anyway, e.g. that the angle for OE_2 is 50°. Especially also we should recall the rule given in Appendix 3 with regard to signs, and change the terminology to suit phasor diagrams, i.e. considering the Real Axis, positive values are to the right of the Imaginary Axis, negative values to the left. Considering the Imaginary Axis, positive values are above the Real Axis, negative values below.

We now have to find the single phasor OR represented by the rectangular coordinates −2.8 (ref.), +7.3 (quad).

By Pythagoras' Theorem

$$OR^2 = 7.3^2 + (-2.8)^2 = 53.29 + 7.84 = 61.13$$

$$\therefore OR = 7.82V$$

$$\text{Tan } \theta = \frac{7.3}{2.8} = 2.607 \qquad \therefore \theta = \tan^{-1} 2.607 = 69°$$

$$\therefore \phi = 180° - 69° = 111°$$

The sum of the two voltages is therefore $7.82V \angle 111°$.

The question did not state whether the two voltages were maximum or rms but this is immaterial, as long as we do not mix the two in the same diagram.

Complex Numbers

The foregoing elementary ideas of phasors, showing how they may be employed for analysis of ac circuits could be all that is required in finding tools for the job because the graphical and calculation methods using them may be employed to solve any circuit. However, an additional system is available through which some of the more difficult manipulations may be reduced in complexity and thereby handled with greater ease. The system is generally known as *Complex Numbers*, but also as *Operator j*. The term "operator" is employed because when any phasor is multiplied by j, the latter operates by rotating that phasor through $90°$ in an anticlockwise direction but with no change in the modulus. Mathematically a complex number is described as a number of which part is real and part imaginary. This complexity is something we must be aware of from the beginning, the numbers serve to continuously describe the rectangular coordinates of phasors yet always keeping separate the two (real and imaginary) parts. Considering that these parts really represent particular points on sinusoidal waveforms separated in time according to the frequency of the waves, we must not fall into the trap here of always using normal algebraic methods, some apply but also some do not. This is a system we use for one purpose only, that is, handling phasors with an angle difference.

Consider a phasor OR as shown in Fig. 1.14(i). It is in the reference position, that is, pointing to the right along the real axis. Suppose it has a magnitude r (volts or amperes). We write down the phasor as $r \angle 0°$ or simply r or +r.

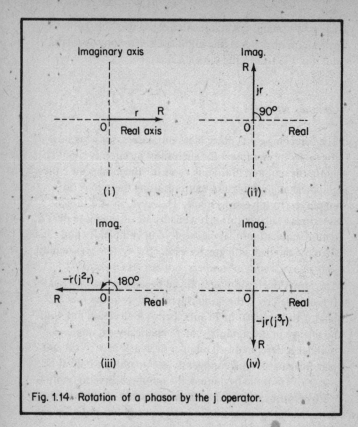

Fig. 1.14 Rotation of a phasor by the j operator.

Now by turning OR through 180° as shown in (iii), from our rule on signs (negative values to left of imaginary axis) it becomes r ∠180° or simply −r because it is in the opposite direction.

If, however, OR is rotated only 90° it becomes in line with the imaginary axis (ii), normally labelled r ∠90°, but in complex notation jr, that is, the j serves to show that OR has been rotated through 90°.

Repeating this last process, stage (iii) could have been

reached by multiplying the jr of stage (ii) itself by j to rotate the phasor through the 90° from 90° to 180°. This gives

$$j \times jr = j^2 r, \quad \text{but (iii) shows the answer to be } -r$$

$$\therefore j^2 r = -r \quad \therefore j^2 = -1 \text{ and } j = \sqrt{-1}$$

this appears to be an oddity for there is no real number root of -1 (in fact all negative numbers squared are positive) and from this comes the term "imaginary". Continuing the process, multiplying again by j, gives at 270° (the imaginary axis again)

$$j \times -r = -jr \quad \text{and further, to } 360°$$

$$j \times -jr = -j^2 r = r \quad (\text{since } j^2 = -1)$$

which makes the labelling of the two axes seem more sensible for the real axis operators are $+1$ and -1 (0° and 180°) and the imaginary axis operators are j and $-j$ (90° and 180°).

In complex notation therefore, a number not preceded by j refers to a component on the real axis, a number preceded by j refers to one on the imaginary axis. But note that we cannot add together algebraically real and imaginary quantities because they do not occur at the same time. That is one of the purposes of the j, it helps us to keep the real and imaginary terms separated until we want to combine them by special rules for changing rectangular coordinates to polar. We are now able to express the rectangular coordinates of a phasor in the form a + jb where a represents the magnitude of the component phasor on the real axis and b that on the imaginary axis as in the following example.

EXAMPLE:
Express the phasors OE_1 and OE_2 of Fig. 1.13(ii) in

41

complex numbers. (The rectangular coordinates for each are already given on the diagram.)

for phasor OE_1 $a = 6.84$ $b = 18.79$
and complex number is 6.84 + j18.79

and for phasor OE_2 $a = -9.64$ $b = -11.49$
and complex number is $-9.64 - j11.49$

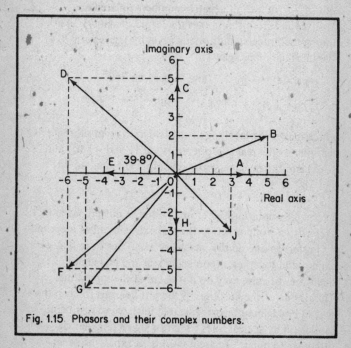

Fig. 1.15 Phasors and their complex numbers.

Further examples of phasors expressed by complex numbers are seen from Fig. 1.15.

Phasor OA is expressed by   3.5 + j0 (i.e. 3.5)
Phasor OB is expressed by   5 + j2
Phasor OC is expressed by   0 + j4.5 (i.e. j4.5)
Phasor OD is expressed by $-6 + j5$

Phasor OE is expressed by $-4 + j0$ (i.e. -4)
Phasor OF is expressed by $-6 - j5$
Phasor OG is expressed by $-5 - j6$
Phasor OH is expressed by $0 - j2.5$ (i.e. $-j2.5$)
Phasor OJ is expressed by $3 - j3$

We pick out OD and OG as a further illustration of conversion and of the effect of multiplication by j.

The modulus of OD $= \sqrt{(-6)^2 + 5^2} = \sqrt{36 + 25} = 7.81$ and the angle (or argument) equals

$$\tan^{-1} \frac{5}{-6} = \tan^{-1} -0.833 = -39.8°$$

From Fig. 1.15 OD is seen to be in the 2nd Quadrant (confirmed by the fact that tan is $-$ in 2nd and 4th Quadrants (Appendix 3, Fig. A3.4)).

$\therefore$ OD makes an angle of $39.8°$ with the real axis as shown and the angle it makes with the reference is $180° - 39.8° = 140.2°$, i.e. OD expressed in polar coordinates is $7.81 \angle 140.2°$.

Similarly for OG, modulus $= \sqrt{(-5)^2 + (-6)^2} = 7.81$

$$\text{argument} = \tan^{-1} \frac{-6}{-5} = \tan^{-1} 1.2 = 50.2°$$

giving a total angle from the reference of $180° + 50.2° = 230.2°$, i.e. OG expressed in polar coordinates is $7.81 \angle 230.2°$.

$\therefore$ OD and OG are at rt. $\angle$s (since $230.2° - 140.2° = 90°$) and of the same modulus.

Now since we have said that multiplication by j rotates a vector through $90°$ in an anticlockwise direction, we must be able to show that multiplying OD by j gives OG:

OD is given by $-6 + j5$

multiply by j:

$$j(-6 + j5) = -j6 + j^2 5 = -j6 - 5 \text{ (since } j^2 = -1),$$

i.e. $-5 - j6$, which is the complex number for OG.

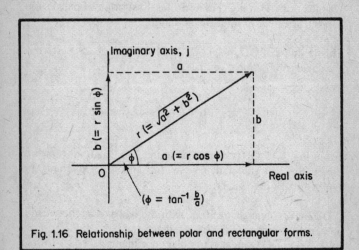

Fig. 1.16 Relationship between polar and rectangular forms.

We can now set down the rules for conversion between polar and rectangular forms. If a phasor is represented in polar form by $r \angle \phi$ and in rectangular form by $a + jb$, (Fig 1.16)

$$\frac{a}{r} = \cos \phi \qquad \therefore a = r \cos \phi$$

$$\frac{b}{r} = \sin \phi \qquad \therefore b = r \sin \phi$$

$$\frac{b}{a} = \tan \phi \qquad \therefore \phi = \tan^{-1} \frac{b}{a}$$

$\therefore$ Rectangular form: $a + jb = r\cos\phi + jr\sin\phi =$

$$r(\cos\phi + j\sin\phi)$$

Polar form:

$$r\angle\phi = \sqrt{a^2 + b^2} \cdot \tan^{-1}\frac{b}{a}$$

Complex Number Algebra:

Most of the rules can be deduced from what has already been discussed, nevertheless it is helpful to set them out for reference.

(i) Addition and Subtraction: Always work so that real and imaginary are kept separate, that is, add or subtract real parts, similarly with imaginary parts. Thus, for two complex numbers $a + jb$ and $c + jd$

$$(a + jb) + (c + jd) = (a + c) + j(b + d)$$

$$(a + jb) - (c + jd) = (a - c) + j(b - d)$$

(ii) Multiplication:

$$(a + jb)(c + jd) = ac + jad + jbc + j^2bd \qquad (j^2 = -1)$$
$$= (ac - bd) + j(ad + bc)$$

$$(a + jb)(c - jd) = ac - jad + jbc - j^2bd \qquad (-j^2 = +1)$$
$$= (ac + bd) + j(bc - ad)$$

(iii) Rationalization: Removing j terms from the denominator of a fraction is called *rationalization*. If the denominator contains only an imaginary term simply multiply numerator and denominator by j, e.g.

$$\frac{a + jb}{jd} \times \frac{j}{j} = \frac{j(a + jb)}{j^2 d} = \frac{ja - b}{-d} \quad \text{(multiply by } -1/-1)$$

$$= \frac{b - ja}{d}$$

If the denominator contains both real and imaginary terms, multiply both numerator and denominator by its *conjugate*, this term is the same except that the sign of the j part is reversed, e.g. the conjugate of a + jb is a − jb. Disappearance of the j part from the denominator follows from the mathematical factorization

$$a^2 - b^2 = (a + b)(a - b)$$

so,

$$\frac{a + jb}{c + jd} = \frac{a + jb}{c + jd} \times \frac{c - jd}{c - jd}$$

((c − jd) is the conjugate of the denominator),

$$= \frac{ac - jad + jbc - j^2bd}{c^2 - (jd)^2} = \frac{(ac + bd) + j(bc - ad)}{c^2 + d^2}$$

or

$$\frac{(ac + bd)}{c^2 + d^2} + j\frac{(bc - ad)}{c^2 + d^2}$$

Rectangular coordinates do not always result in the simplest method, for some calculations the polar form actually needs less arithmetic, experience will show which method to choose.

The polar forms can only be added or subtracted by first changing to rectangular unless the graphical method is used. Conversely multiplication and division are simple directly in polar form.

Multiplication of Polar Form: If $p\angle\theta$ and $r\angle\phi$ are two phasors to be multiplied together then,

$$p\angle\theta \times r\angle\phi = pr\underline{/\theta + \phi}$$

46

and squaring $r\angle\phi$ gives $r^2\underline{/2\phi}$,

square root: $\qquad \sqrt{r\angle\phi} = \sqrt{r} \; \underline{/\phi/2}$

Division of Polar Form:

$$p\angle\theta \div r\angle\phi = \frac{p}{r}\underline{/\theta - \phi}$$

One example on the use of complex numbers follows. The reader will gain more experience as the system is put to use in the next chapter.

EXAMPLE:
Add together the phasors $13\angle22.6°$ and $5\angle323.1°$. Divide the result by $6 - j6$, expressing the final answer in polar form.

Phasor 1, rectangular coordinates,

$$13(\cos 22.6° + j\sin 22.6°) = 12 + j5 \text{ (1st Quadrant)}$$

Phasor 2, rectangular coordinates,

$$5(\cos 323.1° + j\sin 323.1°) \text{ (4th Quadrant, j term negative)}$$

$$= 5(\cos 36.9° - j\sin 36.9°) = 4 - j3$$

(remember that a sketch of the phasors is invaluable in ensuring that the signs are correct)

$$\text{sum} = (12 + j5) + (4 - j3) = \underline{16 + j2}$$

Dividing by $6 - j6$:

$$\frac{16 + j2}{6 - j6}$$

(multiply numerator and denominator by conjugate of denominator)

$$\frac{16 + j2}{6 - j6} \times \frac{6 + j6}{6 + j6} = \frac{96 + j96 + j12 - 12}{6^2 + 6^2} =$$

$$\frac{84 + j108}{72} = 1.167 + j1.5$$

In polar form:

$$\sqrt{1.167^2 + 1.5^2} \; \tan^{-1} \frac{1.5}{1.167} = \sqrt{1.362 + 2.25} \; \tan^{-1} 1.285$$

$$= \underline{1.9 \angle 52.1°}$$

1.4   COMPLEX WAVEFORMS

As is so often the case in electronics, by "complex" is meant "consisting of parts" rather than "complicated" which gives rise to a slightly different impression, although in many cases this latter meaning also applies. The sine wave is a simple waveform, derived as we found earlier, from simple harmonic motion, one of Nature's many technicalities. There is a multiplicity of waves of other shapes and certainly a few of these are worthy of our consideration because from their analysis we derive so much understanding of some of the important but all too often misunderstood transmission principles. The technique we use arises from a theorem produced by Fourier (Jean Baptiste Joseph Fourier, a French mathematician and physicist) which refers to any continuous periodic function, (that is, a continuous waveform with all cycles the same — obviously we cannot produce an equation to a wave which varies from cycle to cycle). The theorem states that such a waveform can be expressed as the sum of a number of sine waves, each having a different amplitude and frequency. It is perhaps difficult to believe at first that a wave which is square and so unlike the smooth sine wave, consists of sine waves and no others after all. Fourier of course, used more advanced mathematics than we have at our disposal, nevertheless much can be done with what we have.

1.4.1 Harmonics

In a complex wave, that is, consisting of several waves of different frequencies adding together, one frequency must be the lowest, this is called the *fundamental*. All others are multiples of the fundamental and are known as *harmonics*, the wave having a frequency twice that of the fundamental is the second harmonic, that having a frequency three times is the third harmonic and so on. The 2nd, 4th, 6th, etc. are the *even harmonics*, the 3rd, 5th, 7th, etc. the *odd harmonics*.

In music, harmony is obtained when two notes have a simple relationship with each other, for example, 2:1. 3:2, 4:3. The first one, 2:1 is called an *octave*, that is one frequency is twice the other. This is equivalent to the 2nd harmonic. Thus the musical note A which has a fundamental frequency at around 400 Hz, becomes an octave higher at 800 Hz and a second octave higher at 1600 Hz. If a pure sine wave at 400 Hz is fed to a loudspeaker, the note A will sound but it will be *pure*, a somewhat unexciting whistle. This is because it is devoid of the harmonics which make the sound harmonious and it is the differences in the harmonic content which distinguish the same note when played on the various musical instruments. Notes from instruments capable of maintaining the sound continuously (the "wind" instruments) could be analysed by the Fourier method although a modern *harmonic analyser*, an instrument capable of separating out and measuring the amplitude of each harmonic, does the job equally well.

There is a further variable to the order (i.e. 2nd, 3rd, 4th, etc.) and amplitude of harmonics present in a complex wave, which is the relative phase of each. Whatever the phase difference between two components, it will be maintained continuously because all components are exact multiples of the fundamental frequency and therefore pass through a complete number of cycles for each cycle of the fundamental. This point and the previous ones are illustrated best by consideration of equations and graphs of "straightforward" complex waveforms.

First consider a sinusoidal waveform represented by $e = E_m$

sin ωt (we could equally work in current, $i = I_m \sin \omega t$, if required). The second harmonic is double the frequency and therefore can be represented by a rotating phasor moving twice as fast, that is, whereas the fundamental wave moves through ωt rads/sec, the 2nd harmonic moves through $2\omega t$ rads/sec. Suppose the harmonic has half the amplitude of the fundamental, its own equation is therefore

$$e = \frac{E_m}{2} \sin 2\omega t$$

Hence the equation to the combined wave is

$$e = E_m \sin \omega t + \frac{E_m}{2} \sin 2\omega t = E_m \left\{ \sin \omega t + \frac{\sin 2\omega t}{2} \right\}$$

We are only interested in the shape of the waveform so we can let $E_m = 1$ and for practice construct a table from which the graphs may be plotted, a suggestion is given in Table 1.1. This table shows a typical layout for the calculations necessary for plotting each graph over one complete cycle. Because most sine tables and calculators work from degrees rather than radians it is convenient to convert first to the former.

The graphs of $E_m \sin \omega t$, $E_m/2 \sin 2\omega t$ and their sum are shown in Fig. 1.17 (i). The X-axis is marked $0 - 2\pi$ rads. for the fundamental and complex waves, strictly the 2nd harmonic should have a second scale $0 - 4\pi$ rads. The change in shape from sinusoidal when the two waveforms are added is clearly shown.

As a further example, the same two waves are again added but in this case the 2nd harmonic lags by $90°$ (i.e. $90°$ for the harmonic, not the fundamental which will only have moved through $45°$). The complex wave is now expressed by

$$e = E_m \sin \omega t + \frac{E_m}{2} \sin (2\omega t - \pi/2)$$

ωt (rads) (1)	Equivalent angle in degrees (2)	sin ωt (3)	2ωt (rads) (4)	Equivalent angle in degrees (5)	sin 2ωt (6)	½ sin 2ωt (7)	sin ωt + ½ sin 2ωt (8)
0	0	0	0	0	0	0	0
0.1π	18	0.3090	0.2π	36	0.5878	0.2939	0.6029
0.2π	36	0.5878	0.4π	72	0.9511	0.4755	1.0633
0.3π	54	0.8090	0.6π	108	0.9511	0.4755	1.2845
......	......	......	......	......	......	......	......
2.0π	360	0	4.0π	720	0	0	0

Col.2 = Col.1 × $\dfrac{180°}{\pi}$

Col.4 = Col.1 × Col.2

Col.5 = Col.4 × $\dfrac{180°}{\pi}$

Col.8 = Col.3 + Col.7

TABLE 1.1 Data for graph of (sin ωt + ½ sin 2ωt)

51

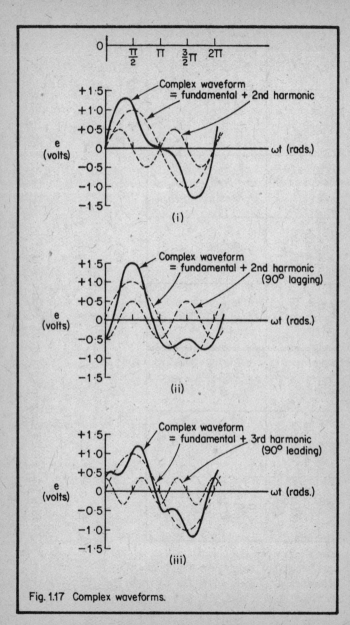

Fig. 1.17 Complex waveforms.

The calculations follow the same pattern as in Table 1.1 except that an additional column is required after Col. 4 headed $(2\omega t - \pi/2)$, subsequent columns being labelled accordingly.

The resultant graphs are shown in Fig. 1.17 (ii). With this phase shift, the complex wave has changed completely, the positive part bearing little resemblance to the negative. A sine wave is *symmetrical* when it is identical above and below the X-axis, the waves we have just produced are not and are said to be *asymmetrical* (the 'a' comes from the Greek, meaning "not"). Fig. 1.17 (ii) is clearly asymmetrical, (i) might be taken as symmetrical but it is not because the peaks do not arise after the same lapse of time from the beginning of the appropriate half-cycle.

These two examples alone are sufficient to demonstrate how we can predict the outcome of the addition of harmonics to a fundamental wave. There is obviously an enormous number of combinations possible but generally it will be found that odd harmonics produce symmetrical complex waves, even harmonics result in asymmetrical ones. One more simple addition of a third harmonic to its fundamental will show the formation of a symmetrical complex wave even when the harmonic is not in phase, as in this example, 90° leading. The equation is

$$e = E_m \sin \omega t + \frac{E_m}{3} \sin (3\omega t + \pi/2)$$

(The amplitude of the harmonic, $E_m/3$, has been chosen for demonstration only, for most complex waves the harmonic amplitude can be of any magnitude. One of the exceptions to this is the square wave, which follows.)

The result is plotted in Fig. 1.17 (iii) and unlike (i) it is seen that the positive and negative half-cycles are identical, a simple test being that, except for the change of sign, the series of figures from which the graph is drawn for each half-cycle is the same.

1.4.2 The Square Wave

We now move on to one of the most important, the *square wave* which simply rises in theoretically no time to its maximum value, maintains this through the first half-cycle and then plunges to an equal value but opposite in sign for the second half-cycle, a waveform easily recognized as symmetrical. Again, we will produce our own from its component parts, identified by Fourier whose equation for a square wave is:

$$e = \frac{4}{\pi} E_m \left(\sin \omega t + \tfrac{1}{3} \sin 3\omega t + \tfrac{1}{5} \sin 5\omega t + \ldots \right)$$

where E_m is the maximum value. The dots at the end of the expression indicate that the series continues to infinity (Appendix 4, Sect. A4.4). From the equation we see that a square wave consists of a fundamental wave plus *all* the *odd* harmonics, successively decreasing in value. By conveniently letting $4\,E_m/\pi = 1$ we can find the shape by calculating the values of the terms in the brackets from $\omega t = 0$ to $\omega t = 2\pi$ using the same procedure as before. We cannot calculate for an infinite number of harmonics, nor is it necessary, for the higher the harmonic, the less it affects the final result. To produce a reasonably square wave we can evaluate the expression up to, say, the 13th harmonic setting out the calculations in the manner shown previously. They are first made with 0.05 steps of ωt, thereafter other intermediate points may be required to define the curve fully, for example points at 0.055 and 0.6π radians for better defining the first peak (Fig. 1.18). There is much work in calculating such a curve (unless a scientific calculator is available) but it does show that we do not have to take the rather complicated Fourier analysis for granted, we can actually test its validity from our own studies of mathematics and trigonometry. The *analysis* of a complex wave means resolving it into its component parts. Alternatively, in Fig. 1.18 we have carried out a *synthesis* of a complex wave by building it up from its component parts.

The term "square wave" is used generally for waves of this

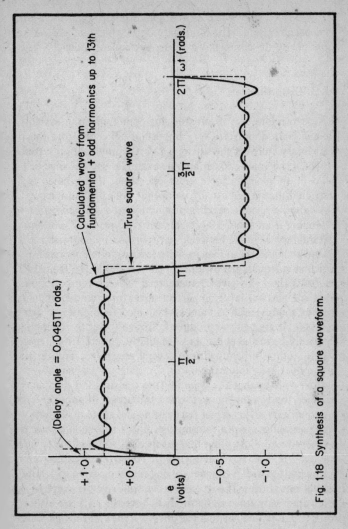

Fig. 1.18 Synthesis of a square waveform.

type, even though, as in Fig. 1.18, the actual shape is rectangular (but note that we can make any rectangular wave square by appropriate choice of graph scales).

The synthesized wave of Fig. 1.18 is very close in shape to the predicted one even when all harmonics higher than the 13th have been omitted. The more harmonics which are added, the more nearly the complex wave becomes square and vice versa.

1.4.3 Distortion

Although a long way from studying communication systems, we can learn about two very important concepts from this elementary study of the square wave. Communication systems, of which the voice and ear are one example, need a range or band of frequencies for correct operation, if the range is restricted the system usually works but not at full efficiency. For example, good speech reproduction needs a *bandwidth* extending from about 100 to somewhat above 6,000 Hz, and an ordinary air-path between two persons in conversation provides this. We can manage with less, as do telephones for which an adequate bandwidth is just over 3,000 Hz, from 300 to 3,400 Hz. This gives "commercial" speech reproduction, good enough, but far from perfect since, for example, sibilants (hissing sounds) such as f and s which have harmonics as high as 6,000 Hz are badly reproduced, thus an f over the telephone can easily be mistaken for an s. Similarly, for colour television which requires a bandwidth of several megahertz, any restriction results in an inferior picture. To transmit a square wave, Fourier tells us that the *channel* (the transmission medium between the two ends) must have a frequency response extending to infinity. This is just not feasible and some of the very high harmonics are not transmitted, thus a true square wave is not received. Illustrating this practically, suppose the square wave of Fig. 1.18 has a frequency of 1000 Hz and the waveform is transmitted over a channel passing frequencies up to 13,000 Hz but not above. The received wave will have the shape of our calculated wave since all harmonics above the 13th are lost in transit, that is, the channel has *distorted* the transmitted waveform. One important effect of this is that there is now a delay before the wave reaches its maximum value. We can bring this to reality for the delay angle is shown on the figure as 0.045π radians. A 1000 Hz wave turns through $2\pi f = 2\pi \times 1000$ rads/sec, hence the actual delay in the wave reaching its maximum value from zero is

$$\frac{0.045\pi \text{ rads}}{2000\pi \text{ rads/sec}} = 22.5 \ \mu s \ ,$$

seemingly a very short period of time but actually quite long in computer and other *digital* systems where information is transmitted in pulses which are in effect very short duration square waves.

Alternatively some systems such as amplifiers may be subject to *overloading* meaning that the output waveform is not an exact replica of the input wave, graphically it becomes flattened or *clipped*. Now if the top of a sine wave is clipped off, the wave is to a certain extent squared and hence some harmonics must be produced. This is usually undesirable, a good example being that of an audio system where music is distorted when incorrect harmonics are present — as all hi-fi enthusiasts know.

1.4.4 Rectification

Transformation of an alternating to a direct current is known as *rectification* and although we have yet to study the devices through which this can be accomplished we can certainly look at the principles from the waveform aspect first. A semi-conductor *diode* (two electrodes) is a device which allows current to flow in one direction only, the symbol used in drawings is shown in Fig. 1.19 (i). Because it originated before electron theory became established, the arrow points in the direction of conventional current flow, that is, when the electrode marked A (anode) is positive relative to the electrode marked K (cathode), current flows through the device. The flow was originally considered to be in the direction of the arrow but we now understand it to be in the opposite direction, that is, electrons flow from K to A as shown. The device can be looked upon as a fast-acting switch as shown in (ii), when A is negative to K the switch is open (off), conversely with A positive to K the switch is closed (on).

57

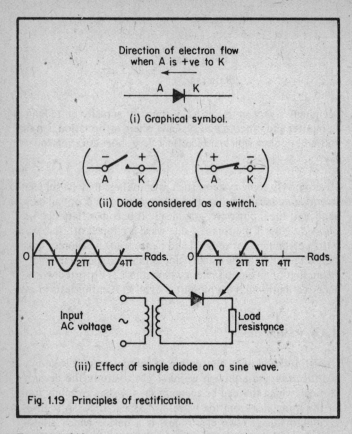

(i) Graphical symbol.

(ii) Diode considered as a switch.

(iii) Effect of single diode on a sine wave.

Fig. 1.19 Principles of rectification.

Fig. 1.19 (iii) shows how an alternating waveform becomes unidirectional simply through the diode allowing the positive half-cycles through but not the negative ones. This is known as *half-wave rectification*, it is clearly a *rough* form of dc, very unlike the steady voltage or current of a battery. Extra diodes and special circuitry however smooth things out.

The resultant waveform in (iii) could not be more asymmetrical and therefore from Fourier analysis we expect it to comprise even harmonics only. If each even harmonic is to enhance the positive half-cycles while reducing the negative ones of the fundamental, it must lag by $90°$, this is demonstrated in Fig.

1.17 (ii) which shows the 2nd harmonic only but even so it is possible to see the effect. Addition of further even harmonics, equally lagging, progressively augments this until the complex waveform reaches that shown in Fig. 1.19 (iii).

Fourier's analysis for the half-wave rectified sine wave is generally expressed as

$$ e = \frac{2E_m}{\pi} \left(0.5 + \frac{\pi}{4} \sin \omega t - \frac{\cos 2\omega t}{3} - \frac{\cos 4\omega t}{15} - \frac{\cos 6\omega t}{35} \cdots \right. $$

$$ \left. - \frac{\cos n\omega t}{n^2 - 1} \right) $$

(in the last term n represents the number of any given even harmonic). This demonstrates that any *non-linear*[A2] device (such as a diode) will produce harmonics in the output wave even when none exist in the input wave.

We can come to terms with the change to cosines in most of the formula from the fact that a sine wave lagging by $\pi/2$ radians, effectively lags on a cosine wave by $\pi/2 + \pi/2 = \pi$ radians, this is equivalent to a cosine wave multiplied by -1, in brief $\sin(\phi - \pi/2) = -\cos \phi$.

This treatment of rectification is mainly for extra experience with wave analysis, a more complete discussion is not appropriate until after an insight into semiconductor theory.

1.5   DISPLAY OF WAVEFORMS BY AN OSCILLOSCOPE

The last of the better known waveforms to be briefly examined in this chapter is the *sawtooth*. Its shape is described by its name and it is appropriate here because one of its uses is in the display of the waveform itself through an instrument designed especially for the purpose, an *oscilloscope* (oscillate, from Latin, "swing" + scope, "to look at").

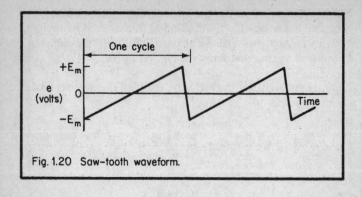

Fig. 1.20 Saw–tooth waveform.

A typical sawtooth waveform is shown in Fig. 1.20. This one rises uniformly from negative to positive for most of the cycle, then suddenly falls to its starting value at the end. Opposite polarity changes also apply. Again, a Fourier series exists for this wave showing that it contains both odd and even harmonics.

One of its important uses is for setting up a *time base*. We have seen how in an elementary cathode-ray tube a narrow beam of electrons can be formed and accelerated along the tube to strike the screen and produce a small bright spot of light, the control being exerted through the principle of like charges repelling, unlike attracting. Consider now the two pairs of electrostatic deflexion plates as shown in Fig. 1.21 (electromagnetic deflexion is also used, but the explanation is slightly more involved), if the potential across the horizontal plates is such that h_l is the more positive, the beam of negative electrons will be deflected to strike the screen at the left-hand side as in (i). With a sawtooth waveform connected across the plates in such a direction as to progressively reduce the positive potential on h_l and increase it on h_r, the spot moves across the screen, linearly with time, to the right-hand side as in (ii). However, near the end of the first cycle of the waveform, it suddenly reverses polarity so causing the spot to fly back to its original position. Subsequent cycles trace out the same path, the constantly repeated left to right movement being sufficient to illuminate a line on the screen. The waveform is said to be producing a time base according to its frequency, (iii).

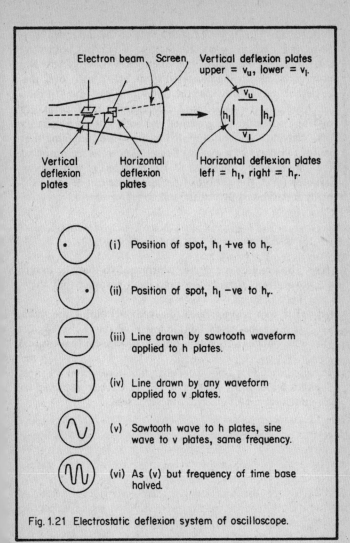

Fig. 1.21 Electrostatic deflexion system of oscilloscope.

Now, if we wish to display an unknown waveform, this is applied across the vertical deflexion plates, producing simply a vertical line if no time base is running (iv). But if a time base waveform is applied to the h-plates at the same time and adjusted in frequency to exactly that of the unknown waveform, it is easy to appreciate that, provided that both waves start together, a graph of the unknown will be drawn. Not only is the spot being deflected from left to right over the cycle but up and down at the same time according to the amplitude of the waveform being examined, hence at any instant its position is governed by both sets of potentials (v). Halving the frequency of the time base (doubling the period) displays two cycles of the unknown waveform since the time taken by the spot to travel from left to right is now doubled (vi). The period of the time base can in fact be many multiples of that of the unknown waveform.

Two special arrangements are worthy of mention.

(i) The oscilloscope circuit is arranged so that the input waveform *triggers* the time base, ensuring that they keep in step.
(ii) The spot is suppressed (blacked-out) during the flyback period otherwise a faint image of whatever exists across the v-plates during that time would appear (backwards).

The oscilloscope is a powerful analytical tool. Even the most complex waveforms, or parts of them, are easily displayed and experimental circuit changes quickly assessed.

2. TIME CONSTANTS

This chapter, although quite small and seemingly squeezed in between two large ones is important as a link joining the two together. It is mainly concerned with a study of the time it takes to fully charge a capacitor or to set up a magnetic field around an inductor. Although much of what we learn arises from the application of d.c. to these components, it is by an understanding of the principles involved that we shall better appreciate reactance when we meet it in the early part of the next chapter for an alternating current is no more than a series of very short duration direct currents but changing in polarity.

2.1 THE RESISTIVE CIRCUIT

There is no question of time when Ohm's Law, $I = E/R$, is considered. The change in I if E changes is so incredibly fast that we consider it to be instantaneous. This is because resistance has no reaction to change, only resistance to current flow itself.

2.2 CAPACITIVE TIME CONSTANT

When capacitance is added to a resistive circuit, a reaction to current change occurs. If there were no resistance, a voltage applied to the capacitor would immediately drive a current into the plates to charge them according to the relationship $Q = CV$. But there is resistance intentionally or unintentionally and as soon as a current commences to flow, voltage is lost across the resistance so that the charge flow into the plates is reduced and hence there is delay in building up the full charge. The higher the resistance, the greater the delay for a given capacitor. Consider the circuit of Fig. 2.1 where R represents the total circuit resistance, including that of the battery.

With switch S in position 1, the capacitor is charged from the battery until the voltage v_c across it is the same as that of the

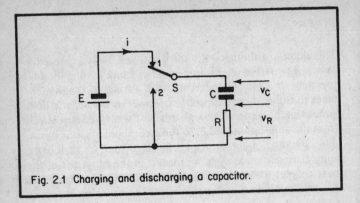

Fig. 2.1 Charging and discharging a capacitor.

battery, these two voltages then being equal and in opposition, current ceases. If the switch is subsequently moved to position 2 the capacitor itself provides the voltage which drives the discharge current through R until eventually all the energy stored has been dissipated as heat loss by the passage of the current through R. We are interested in the time taken for these things to happen.

When the switch S is first operated, no charge is held by C and therefore there is no opposing voltage ($v_c = 0$), hence the instantaneous circuit current $i = E/R$. However, immediately i starts to flow, a voltage builds up across the capacitor because of its charge and the charging current falls to

$$i = \frac{E - v_c}{R}$$

The capacitor continues to charge, but at a lower rate, v_c increases and eventually when $v_c = E$, $i = 0$.

Obviously a graph showing, for example, the charge on the capacitor as time progresses is needed. Fortunately for a given capacitor, since $Q/V = C$ and C is constant, we can use the voltage v_c across C as an indication of the charge and in fact, frequently we talk about a capacitor charged to so many volts when strictly we mean charged with so many coulombs.

Let us see how to build up our own time graph of v_c first. We must consider very small time intervals (say, 10 ms) for the assumption has to be made that the current during each interval is constant. Consider Fig. 2.2 which is a practical circuit in which C and R are so chosen that their product is 1, this helps to keep the arithmetic at a minimum.

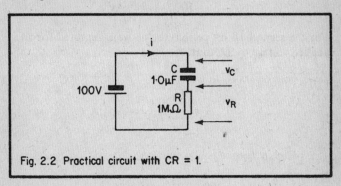

Fig. 2.2 Practical circuit with CR = 1.

The capacitor is charging and the quantity q of charge held at any instant is q (coulombs) = C × v_c, where C is the capacity in Farads and v_c is the voltage across C.

Also

$$q \text{ (coulombs)} = i \text{ (amps)} \times t \text{ (seconds)}$$

$$\therefore \quad v_c = \frac{i \times t}{C}$$

We consider what changes take place in each 10 ms period:

(1) When the 100 V is first applied the current is limited only by R and is therefore

$$\frac{100}{1 \times 10^6} \text{ amps} = 100 \, \mu A$$

(2) During the first 10 ms period v_c rises from 0 V to

$$\frac{it}{C} = \frac{100 \times 10^{-6} \times 10 \times 10^{-3}}{1 \times 10^{-6}} = 1.0 \text{ V}$$

(3) When $v_c = 1$ V, the effective voltage (i.e. the voltage capable of further charging the capacitor) is

$$100 - 1 = 99 \text{ V}$$

For the second 10 ms period, the above is repeated for an applied voltage of 99, thus:

(4) With 99 V effective,

$$i = \frac{99}{1 \times 10^6} = 99 \, \mu\text{A}$$

(5) Rise in v_c over period equals

$$\frac{it}{C} = \frac{99 \times 10^{-6} \times 10 \times 10^{-3}}{1 \times 10^{-6}} = 0.99 \text{ V}$$

(6) Total v_c after 20 ms = 1.0 + 0.99 = 1.99 V.

(7) Effective charging voltage at end of period

$$= 100 - 1.99 = 98.01 \text{ V}$$

Table 2.1 shows these calculations for the first 100 ms. There is no point in continuing for the whole 5 seconds necessary to produce the complete curve because this exercise is only designed to provide us with a more intimate knowledge of how the capacitor charges. What is noteworthy from the table is the fact that each time v_c increases it causes the charging current to fall so that during each time interval the rise in v_c is controlled by its own value in the previous interval. This

10 ms Period Number	Total Time Elapsed (ms)	Current (i) held at (µA)	Rise in v_c over period (V)	Total v_c (V)	Effective voltage at end of period (V)	Current for next period (µA)
1	10	100	1.0	1.0	99	99
2	20	99	0.99	1.99	98.01	98.01
3	30	98.01	0.9801	2.9701	97.0299	97.0299
4	40	97.0299	0.9703	3.9404	96.0596	96.0596
5	50	96.0596	0.9606	4.9010	95.0990	95.0990
6	60	95.0990	0.9510	5.8520	94.1480	94.1480
7	70	94.1480	0.9415	6.7935	93.2065	93.2065
8	80	93.2065	0.9321	7.7256	92.2744	92.2744
9	90	92.2744	0.9227	8.6483	91.3517	91.3517
10	100	91.3517	0.9135	9.5618	90.4382	90.4382
......	......	......	......	......	......	......

TABLE 2.1   Calculation of v_c and i for circuit of Figure 2.2 (10 ms periods)

sequence brings us to Appendix 4, Section 2, where we find that epsilon (e) enters the scene. In fact the capacitor is charging according to an exponential of epsilon, the charge q after any time, t seconds being

$$q = Q(1 - e^{-t/CR})$$

where Q is the maximum charge and since

$$\frac{q}{C} = v_c \quad \text{and} \quad \frac{Q}{C} = E,$$

dividing the above by C gives

$$v_c = E(1 - e^{-t/CR})$$

The product CR in the denominator of the exponent is known as the *time constant* of that particular circuit. It is given the symbol τ (Greek letter, tau) and when C is in Farads and R in ohms, τ is in seconds.

As t increases, for a fixed value of CR, e^t increases but e^{-t} (i.e. $1/e^t$) decreases, thus the bracketed quantity approaches 1, v_c rising until it is equal to the battery voltage E as one might expect. The rise in v_c in the early stages can be seen in Table 2.1. Also the table shows in the last column the fall in the charging current and this is given by the formula

$$i = \frac{E}{R} \cdot e^{-t/CR},$$

hence as t increases, i decreases, theoretically to zero.

We meet again one of those electronic peculiarities — the capacitor never really becomes fully charged! Whatever the value of t, say 1 minute, (which is often a long time in electronics), $e^{-t/CR}$ for our circuit equals 8.76×10^{-27}, be it ever so small, it does have some value and therefore v_c is not quite equal to E, nor is i quite zero. So we have to adopt some

convention to tell us when a capacitor is considered to be
fully charged and this is when t is equal to 5 times the time
constant. We shall understand this more clearly by examining
the graph of v_c for the circuit of Fig. 2.2, this is shown in
Fig. 2.3. Note that for this particular circuit the time constant
$C \times R = 1$ s. Help with calculations involving powers of e is
given in Appendix 4, Section 2.1.

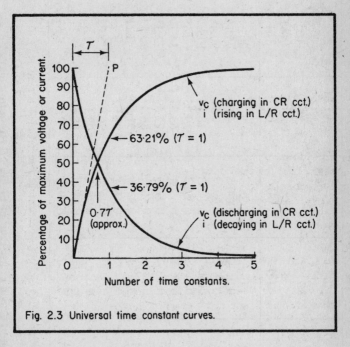

Fig. 2.3 Universal time constant curves.

Calculation of the curve points is shown in Table 2.2.
Comparing equal values of t (e.g. at 50 and 100 ms) with
Table 2.1 shows how closely the calculations agree, those from
Table 2.2 being correct since the actual increments of v_c are
continuous, not stepped[A4.2].

By choosing a battery voltage of 100 for the example and
labelling the X-axis in seconds we have in fact produced a
universal curve provided that the axis labels are changed to

69

"Percentage of maximum voltage or current" and "Number of Time-Constants (secs)" for in these terms the curve applies to any other CR circuit. As an example the curve illustrates the fact that "full charge" is virtually achieved after a period of time equal to 5τ. Also after $\tau = 1$, v_c has risen to 63.21% of the full voltage. These two features are useful because once

Time Elapsed, t (1)	$\dfrac{t}{CR}$ (2)	$e^{-t/CR}$ (3)	$1 - e^{-t/CR}$ (4)	$v_c = 100(1 - e^{-t/CR})$ (volts) (5)	$i = e^{-t/CR} \times 10^2$ (μA) (6)
0	0	1.0	0	0	100
50 ms	0.05	0.9512	0.0488	4.88	95.12
100 ms	0.1	0.9048	0.0952	9.52	90.48
200 ms	0.2	0.8187	0.1813	18.13	81.87
500 ms	0.5	0.6065	0.3935	39.35	60.65
1.0 s	1.0	0.3679	0.6321	63.21	36.79
1.5 s	1.5	0.2231	0.7769	77.69	22.31
2.0 s	2.0	0.1353	0.8647	86.47	13.53
2.5 s	2.5	0.0821	0.9179	91.79	8.21
3.0 s	3.0	0.0498	0.9502	95.02	4.98
3.5 s	3.5	0.0302	0.9698	96.98	3.02
4.0 s	4.0	0.0183	0.9817	98.17	1.83
4.5 s	4.5	0.0111	0.9889	98.89	1.11
5.0 s	5.0	0.0067	0.9933	99.33	0.67

(For "Universal Curve", Col. 5 gives percentage rise if Col. 1 is read as τ)

TABLE 2.2   Calculation of v_c and i for circuit of Figure 2.2 (from formula)

having calculated τ, much is known about the curves. In addition v_c rises to 86.5% after 2τ and 95% after 3τ.

If the whole process is repeated for a capacitor discharging through a resistance (i.e. switch changed to position 2 after C has been fully charged, Fig. 2.1) a discharge curve for v_c is obtained as shown on Fig. 2.3.

In this case no battery is involved, therefore E = 0 and the voltage equation changes to

$$v_c = Ve^{-t/CR}$$

where V is the potential to which C was originally charged.

We see also that after $\tau = 1$, v_c (discharging) has fallen to 36.79% of its original value, i.e. C has discharged 63.21%.

Thus the time constant indicates the *rate* of charge or discharge since it shows the time in seconds for a 63.21% change to take place.

It is now possible to develop a second definition. Considering Fig. 2.1, the initial current = E/R and since at any instant

$$q = C \times v_c = i \times t$$

initially

$$C \times v_c = (E/R) \times T$$

$$\therefore \quad t = C \times v_c \div \frac{E}{R} = CR \times \frac{v_c}{E}$$

Now if the initial current continued to flow, the capacitor would be fully charged when $v_c = E$, i.e. when t = CR seconds.

We can therefore also define the time constant as the time taken for the capacitor to become fully charged if the current continued at its initial value. This is shown on Fig. 2.3 where the line OP is a tangent to the charging curve at point O and therefore has the same slope. It meets the 100% voltage level at P, one time constant along. We can check on the slope by referring to the practical example in Table 2.1 where the initial rise in v_c is 1.0 V (in the first 10 ms period). If this rate of rise is maintained, v_c will reach 100 V in 100 × 10 ms = 1 second, which is equal to τ for the circuit.

EXAMPLE:
A 9 V battery is connected across a 0.01 μF capacitor in series with a 100 kΩ resistor. If the resistance of the battery is negligible, what is the time constant of the circuit and what will the voltages be across both capacitor and resistor after 2 ms?

$$E = 9 \text{ V}$$
$$C = 0.01 \times 10^{-6} \text{ F}$$
$$R = 10^5 \, \Omega$$
$$t = 0.002 \text{ s}$$
$$v_c = ?$$
$$v_R = ?$$

Time constant,

$$\tau = C \times R = 0.01 \times 10^{-6} \times 10^5 \text{ s} = \underline{0.001 \text{ s}}$$

By calculation from formula:

$v_c = E(1 - e^{-t/CR})$ $t/CR = 0.002/0.001 = 2$

$\quad = 9(1 - e^{-2})$ $[e^{-2} = \text{antilog}_{10}(-2 \times 0.4343)$

$\quad = 9(1 - 0.1353)$ $\quad = \text{antilog}_{10} -0.8686$

$\quad = 9 \times 0.8647$ $\quad = \text{antilog}_{10} \overline{1}.1314$

$\quad = \underline{7.7823 \text{ V}}$ $\quad = 0.1353]$

and $v_R = 9 - 7.7823 = \underline{1.2177 \text{ V}}$

By use of Table 2.2: since t = 2τ, v_c has risen to 86.47% of the full value of 9 V, i.e.

$$v_c = 0.8647 \times 9 = \underline{7.7823 \text{ V}}$$

EXAMPLE:
Using the percentages given by the universal curves of Fig. 2.3 (figures in Table 2.2) sketch the capacitor voltage/time characteristics for a 50 V battery of negligible internal resistance when connected across a capacitor of 2 μF in series with a resistor of 2 kΩ. Repeat for double the capacity and again for double the resistance.

τ_1 for 2 μF/2 kΩ = $2 \times 10^{-6} \times 2 \times 10^3$ = 0.004 s
τ_2 for 4 μF/2 kΩ = $4 \times 10^{-6} \times 2 \times 10^3$ = 0.008 s
τ_3 for 2 μF/4 kΩ = $2 \times 10^{-6} \times 4 \times 10^3$ = 0.008 s

First circuit:

v_c at $1 \times \tau$ = 0.632	$\times$ 50 V = 31.6 V		t = 4 ms
v_c at $2 \times \tau$ = 0.8647	$\times$ 50 V = 43.2 V		t = 8 ms
v_c at $3 \times \tau$ = 0.950	$\times$ 50 V = 47.5 V		t = 12 ms
v_c at $4 \times \tau$ = 0.982	$\times$ 50 V = 49.1 V		t = 16 ms
v_c at $5 \times \tau$ = 0.993	$\times$ 50 V = 49.7 V		t = 20 ms

These values are used to sketch the characteristic shown in Fig. 2.4.

The 2nd and 3rd circuits have equal time constants, therefore v_c for each will follow the same characteristic but to a time scale double that of the 1st circuit.

This example demonstrates the fact that for a fixed value of resistance, a larger value of capacitance requires a longer time for full charge, also for a given capacitance, increasing the resistance increases the charging time because the current flow is reduced.

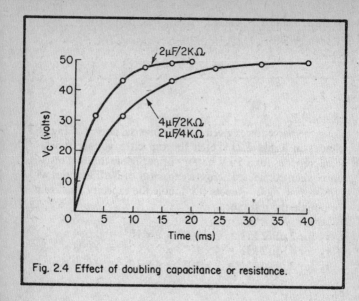

Fig. 2.4 Effect of doubling capacitance or resistance.

EXAMPLE:

A photographic flash unit which needs a heavy current is operated by discharging a capacitor on operation of switch S as shown in Fig. 2.5. What discharge current flows immediately S is operated and how long is it until the capacitor is fully discharged?

Time constant of capacitor + flash unit = C x R =

$$200 \times 10^{-6} \times 2.5 = 5 \times 10^{-4} \text{ s}$$

Assuming C is charged to 18 V, initial discharge current = 18/2.5 = 7.2 A

C is fully discharged after 5 τ s, i.e.

$$5 \times 5 \times 10^{-4} \text{ s} = 2.5 \text{ ms}$$

Thus a small battery, only capable of directly providing a current of the order of mA, can through the medium of a

capacitor, produce a short-duration heavy current commencing
in this example at 7.2 A but falling to zero within about
2.5 ms.

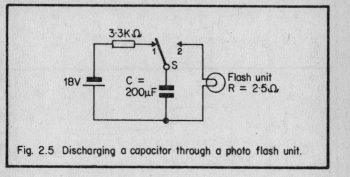

Fig. 2.5 Discharging a capacitor through a photo flash unit.

2.3   INDUCTIVE TIME CONSTANT

We have seen earlier that inductance also resists current change
thus raising the question as to whether time is needed for the
current in an inductor to rise or fall. This is so and many of
the principles involved follow closely those for capacitance.
An inductor has its own unavoidable wire resistance but this
can electrically be considered as being in series with a pure
(i.e. no resistance) inductance as shown in Fig. 2.6.

With switch S moved to position 1, a current i starts to flow
through the inductor L and resistor R, the latter produces a
voltage drop v_R = iR while the current in the inductor
commences to set up a magnetic flux. The rising flux creates a
back or counter-emf in the turns of the inductor with the
relationship E = v_L + v_R always holding because the battery
is maintaining the voltage E across L and R in series.

Now from our earlier studies on inductance we found that the
back-emf (which is now labelled v_L) is:

$$v_L = L \times \frac{\text{(change in current)}}{\text{time}}$$

75

and we can rearrange this as

$$\text{(change in current)} = \frac{v_L \times \text{time}}{L}$$

where time is in seconds and L is in henrys.

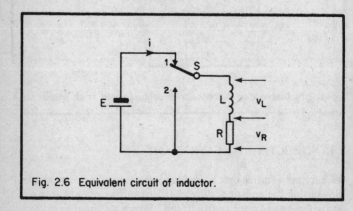

Fig. 2.6 Equivalent circuit of inductor.

This gives the sort of relationship necessary for construction of
a graph of the rise of current in an inductance with time, as in
the case of capacitance. If again very short periods of time are
considered, by looking at the current at the beginning of a
period, the voltage dropped across R can be calculated thereby
enabling v_L to be determined. From the formula the current
change is then found, hence the current at the end of the
period which in fact is the beginning of the next period. Short
periods of time must be used because we have to assume that
v_L remains constant over the period; actually it does not so
we are likely to find a small discrepancy between this method
and the formula involving epsilon which will be developed
subsequently. Nevertheless, it is good practice to follow
through a few calculations to get to grips with what happens
in the circuit as time progresses.

Again, for convenience we choose a circuit requiring minimum
arithmetic, this occurs when the time constant $L/R = 1$, the

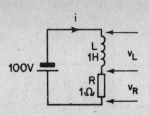

Fig. 2.7 Practical circuit with L/R = 1.

practical circuit is shown in Fig. 2.7. To identify the instantaneous currents in each period of time subscripts to i are used with the period number, that is, in period 4 the current changes from i_3 to i_4.

(1)   During the first period of 10 ms

$$(i_1 - i_0) = \frac{v_L \times t}{L} = \frac{100 \times 0.01}{1} = 1.0 \text{ A}$$

[This checks because the current is changing at a rate of 1 A in 0.01 s, i.e. 100 A/s and from the definition of the henry for which a current change of 1 A/s induces an emf of 1 V, 100 A/s must induce 100 V to be equal and opposite to the 100 V battery]
i.e. i_1, the current at the end of period 1 = 1.0A.

(2)   If 1 A flows, there will be a voltage drop across R of 1 A × 1 Ω = 1 V, leaving 99 V across L for period 2.

(3)   Repeating for period 2:

$$(i_2 - i_1) = \frac{99 \times 0.01}{1} = 0.99 \text{ A}$$

but since i_1 = 1 A, i_2 = 0.99 A + i_1 = 1.99 A.

77

(4) With 1.99 A flowing, the voltage drop across R increases to 1.99 V, leaving 98.01 V across L for period 3.

10 ms Period Number	Total Time Elapsed (ms)	Increase in current over period (A)	Total Current i (A)	v_R (V)	v_L (V)
1	10	1.0	1.0	1.0	99
2	20	0.99	1.99	1.99	98.01
3	30	0.9801	2.9701	2.9701	97.0299
4	40	0.9703	3.9404	3.9404	96.0596
5	50	0.9606	4.9010	4.9010	95.0990
6	60	0.9510	5.8520	5.8520	94.1480
7	70	0.9415	6.7935	6.7935	93.2065
8	80	0.9321	7.7256	7.7256	92.2744
9	90	0.9227	8.6483	8.6483	91.3517
10	100	0.9135	9.5618	9.5618	90.4382
……	……	……	……	……	……

TABLE 2.3 Calculation of v_L for circuit of Figure 2.7 (10 ms periods)

Table 2.3 contains these calculations for the first 100 ms and comparison with Table 2.1 shows much similarity in the figures because in fact both the battery voltages and the time constants are the same in the two cases.

We note that each time i increases it causes v_L to fall because of the rise in v_R and hence the rise in i during the next period is lessened. Therefore during each time interval the rise in current is controlled by its own value in the previous interval bringing us via Appendix 4, Section 2, to epsilon and the formula

$$i = \frac{E}{R} (1 - e^{-Rt/L})$$

or

$$i = I (1 - e^{-Rt/L})$$

where I is the maximum current.

In the capacitive case t in the exponent of e is divided by the time constant CR. Similarly in the inductive case, t is divided by the time constant L/R $(t \div L/R = Rt/L)$ where L is in henrys, R in ohms. The general symbol for time constant τ is also used.

The figures in Table 2.2 also apply for inductance, the column headings being amended as follows:

Col. 2 Heading $\dfrac{Rt}{L}$ since for $\tau = 1$ in both cases, $\dfrac{t}{CR} = \dfrac{Rt}{L}$

Col. 3 For the same reason, change to $e^{-Rt/L}$

Col. 4 Change to $1 - e^{-Rt/L}$

Col. 5   Since $\dfrac{E}{R} = 100$ A, change to i $= 100(1 - e^{-Rt/L})$ amps

Col. 6   Since i $= 100(1 - e^{-Rt/L})$ amps, then
$v_R = 100(1 - e^{-Rt/L}) \times 1$ volts and
$v_L = 100 - 100(1 - e^{-Rt/L})$ volts
$= 100 - 100 + 100e^{-Rt/L}$ volts,
i.e. $v_L = e^{-Rt/L} \times 10^2$ volts.

The universal curves of Fig. 2.3 also apply and are marked accordingly.

When in Fig. 2.6, switch S is operated to position 2, the magnetic flux surrounding the inductor collapses and in so doing produces an emf in the winding which opposes the collapse of the current (Lenz's Law). The energy of the magnetic flux is dissipated as heat in the resistance R, the current decay curve being expressed by

$$i = \frac{E}{R} \ e^{-Rt/L}$$

or

$$i = I \cdot e^{-Rt/L}$$

where I is the maximum current — in this case the commencing current.

EXAMPLE:
In the circuit of Fig. 2.7 how long does it take for i to reach maximum value (i) with the battery voltage 100 as shown, (ii) with a 10 V battery?

(i) $\tau = \dfrac{L}{R} = \dfrac{1}{1} = 1$s

∴ Time for i to reach maximum $= 5\tau$ s $= \underline{5 \text{ s}}$

(ii) The time taken is independent of battery voltage, i.e. time to reach maximum = 5 s.

EXAMPLE:
An inductor of 5 H and resistance 20 Ω is connected to a battery and then to a discharge resistor of 80 Ω. How long will it take for the discharge current to fall to half?

Let maximum current = I, then i = 0.5 I. Total R = 80 + 20 = 100 Ω.

$$\tau = \frac{L}{R} = \frac{5}{100} = 0.05 \text{ s}$$

from the formula: $i = I \cdot e^{-Rt/L}$

∴ $0.5 I = I \cdot e^{-Rt/L}$

∴ $0.5 = e^{-Rt/L}$

[t is hidden away in the exponent of e so we must bring it out of this position first. This is done by taking logs of both sides for $\log_e e^x$ is simply x.]

∴ $$\log_e 0.5 = -\frac{Rt}{L}$$

∴ $$t = -\frac{L}{R} \times \log_e 0.5$$

The calculation of $\log_e 0.5$ is really going to test our skill with logarithms:

(i) Suppose we have tables of natural (Napierian) logs available, the tables usually give logs of numbers between 1 and 10 only, so

$$\log_e 0.5 = \log_e(5 \times 10^{-1}) = \log_e 5 + \log_e 10^{-1}$$

$$= 1.6094 + \overline{3}.6974 \text{ (from tables)}$$

$$= \overline{1}.3068 = -1 + 0.3068 = \underline{-0.6932}$$

(ii) If common log tables only are available, from Appendix 4, Section 2.2

$$\log_e 0.5 = \frac{\log_{10} 0.5}{0.4343}$$

Now, $\log_{10} 0.5 = \overline{1}.6990 = -1 + -0.6990 = -0.3010.$

$$\therefore \qquad \log_e 0.5 = \frac{-0.3010}{0.4343}$$

presenting us with a fraction which itself needs to be calculated out by logarithms:

$\log_{10} 0.3010$ (a)	=	$\overline{1}.4786$
$\log_{10} 0.4343$ (b)	=	$\overline{1}.6378$
$\log_{10} a/b$	=	$\overline{1}.8408$
antilog	=	0.6931

i.e. $\log_e 0.5 = \underline{-0.6931}$

Returning to the calculation of

$$t = -\frac{L}{R} \times \log_e 0.5$$

$$t = -0.05 \times -0.6931$$

$$= \underline{0.03466 \text{ secs}}$$

An approximate answer is given immediately by Fig. 2.3 which shows that the 50% current or voltage point occurs at 0.7τ approximately, hence

$$t = 0.05 \times 0.7 = \underline{0.035 \text{ s approx.}}$$

EXAMPLE:
A 10 V battery is connected to an inductor of 0.5 H and resistance 500 Ω. What is the current in the circuit at t = 0, 1, 2 and 3 ms?

By calculation from formula:

$$\tau = \frac{L}{R} = \frac{0.5}{500} = 0.001 \text{ s}$$

$$\therefore \qquad \frac{Rt}{L} = 1000 \, t$$

At $t = 0$

$$i_0 = \frac{10}{500} \, (1 - e^{-1000 \times 0}) = 0.02 \, (1 - 1) = \underline{0}$$

At t = 1 ms

$$i_1 = \frac{10}{500} \, (1 - e^{-1000 \times 0.01}) = 0.02 \, (1 - e^{-1})$$

$$\therefore \qquad i_1 = 0.02 \, (1 - 0.3679)$$

$$= 0.02 \times (0.6321) = 0.01264 \text{ A}$$

$$= \underline{12.64 \text{ mA}}$$

$[e^{-1} = \text{antilog}_{10}(-1 \times 0.4343)$
$= \text{antilog}_{10} -0.4343 = \text{antilog}_{10} \, \overline{1}.5657$
$= 0.3679]$

The reader may wish to try calculating for t = 2 ms (17.29 mA) and t = 3 ms (19.0 mA).

Alternatively, by use of Universal Curves (Fig. 2.3 or Table 2.2) since $\tau = 0.001$ s, 1 ms, 2 ms and 3 ms are equivalent to 1τ, 2τ and 3τ.

$\therefore$ When $t = 1$ ms, $i_1 = 63.21\%$ of 0.02 A
$\qquad\qquad = 0.02 \times 0.6321$
$\qquad t = 2$ ms, $i_2 = 86.47\%$ of 0.02 A
$\qquad\qquad = 0.02 \times 0.8647$
$\qquad t = 3$ ms, $i_3 = 95.02\%$ of 0.02 A
$\qquad\qquad = 0.02 \times 0.9502$

all as calculated above.

2.4   INTERRUPTING AN INDUCTIVE CIRCUIT

An interesting phenomenon which has made itself known to many experimenters in a rather painful manner is the very high back or counter-emf which arises when the current in an inductive circuit suddenly ceases. Such a high voltage can also make itself known in other ways, for example by causing arcing at switch contacts. Electrical switches take many different forms but basically most are "on" when two pieces of metal connected to the circuit (usually consisting of small blades or points) are in close contact; electrons flow across the point of contact especially if the surfaces are plated with a suitable precious metal such as silver or platinum. The switch is "off" when these two contacts are mechanically separated to leave a small gap, the circuit is then broken except for the very high resistance of the switch mechanism itself.

Fig. 2.8 shows a typical switch (in more detail than a circuit symbol) connected to the coil of, for example, an electromagnetic relay (a switch electromagnetically operated) but simply represented here by an inductance of 5 H and resistance of 1000 Ω. When the switch contacts are closed, the maximum circuit current of 50/1000 = 50 mA flows. As the switch contacts begin to part it is more than likely that an unwanted spark will jump across the tiny gap, unwanted

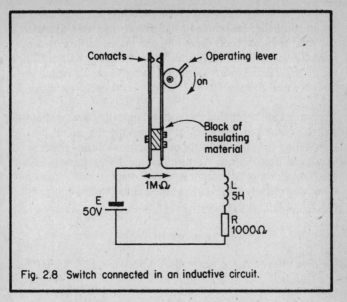

Fig. 2.8 Switch connected in an inductive circuit.

because it burns away the contacts due to intense heat over a tiny area. Sparks or *arcing* arise when a sufficiently high voltage between the contacts is impressed across a small air-gap, then even electrons which are normally tightly bound to their atoms are forced away, ionizing the air and forming a conducting path. A current then flows with sufficient heat generated to form a tiny arc.

When the switch contacts are closed,

$$\tau_c = \frac{L}{R} = \frac{5}{1000} = 5 \times 10^{-3} \text{ s.}$$

Let us suppose that the switch itself has a resistance of 1 MΩ, mainly that of the block of insulating material shown, then when the contacts are open,

$$\tau_0 = \frac{5}{10^6} = 5 \times 10^{-6} \text{ s}$$

(neglecting R which is small in comparison), that is, because of the much higher resistance in the circuit, the time constant has been reduced 1000 times and the magnetic flux of the inductor will collapse very quickly, i.e. within $5\tau = 25 \times 10^{-6}$ s, i.e. 25 μs. The 50 mA of current flowing when the switch is on is reduced to zero within 25 μs of the contacts opening.

We can get some idea of the voltage appearing across the switch contacts at the moment of breaking the circuit by considering the rate of change of the current during the first very small time interval. It must be a small interval because the rate of change of current is not constant, it starts high and then progressively falls. Let us take a time interval equivalent to 0.01 of the time constant. Then since

$$\tau_0 = 5 \times 10^{-6} \text{ s}$$

the time interval $(t_0 \text{ to } t_1) = 0.01 \times 5 \times 10^{-6}$ s $= 5 \times 10^{-8}$ s

Now $\qquad i = I\,e^{-Rt/L} \qquad \dfrac{Rt}{L} = \dfrac{10^6 \times 5 \times 10^{-8}}{5} = 0.01$

$\therefore \qquad i = I e^{-0.01} = I \times 0.9900$

$\therefore$ Change of current during interval is

$$I - 0.99I = 0.01I$$

$$= 0.01 \times 0.05 \text{ A} = 0.0005 \text{ A}$$

and rate of change of current is

$$0.0005 \text{ A in } (5 \times 10^{-8}) \text{ s} = \frac{0.0005}{5} \times 10^8 = 10^4 \text{ A/s}$$

Hence back, or counter-emf

$$e = L \times \text{rate of change of current}$$

$$= 5 \times 10^4 = 50{,}000 \text{ volts,}$$

a truly enormous voltage and although gone in a flash, it is easy to appreciate how the tiny air-gap between the switch contacts breaks down as they open. When this consistently occurs, the contacts become pitted and burn away, eventually causing bad (high resistance) contact .

2.4.1 Spark Quenches

There are several types of *spark-quench* circuit, the simplest being to shunt (connect in parallel) a resistor across the contacts so that τ_0 is increased and the back-emf reduced, certain voltage-sensitive resistors (i.e. the resistance falls as voltage increases) also have a special application for this purpose. The shunting resistance may, however, have undesired effects on the normal circuit, in which case the capacitor spark quench, although more expensive, may be efficient. Two practical circuits are shown in Fig. 2.9. In (i) when the contacts open, the voltage which would be developed across them instead causes a charge to flow into the capacitor to which effectively the energy previously stored in the inductance, is transferred. When the contacts close again, C discharges through them. However, this latter action could result in a relatively heavy current from C causing the tiny

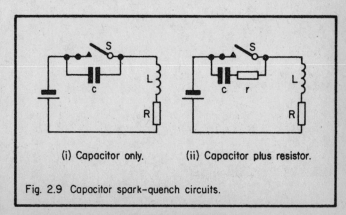

     (i) Capacitor only.   (ii) Capacitor plus resistor.

Fig. 2.9 Capacitor spark-quench circuits.

contacts to weld because of the heating effect of a large current flowing across a small area. Thus circuit (ii) may be preferable in which the current is limited by resistor r.

A single spark-quench capacitor is used in motor car engines across the "points" of the contact-breaker in the ignition system to reduce arcing, it is effective although not fully, hence the move to all-electronic systems which avoid the use of mechanical switching.

3. ALTERNATING CURRENT CIRCUITS

We have seen time and time again how important Ohm's Law is in electronic circuit analysis for what matter most in any circuit are current and voltage. If the resistance is known in a d.c. circuit and one of these, the other follows. Thus when we come to study the effect of capacitance or inductance we need some parameter equivalent to resistance to describe the opposition these two circuit constituents offer to alternating current flow in a similar manner to that in a direct current circuit so that Ohm's Law still applies. This in fact is called *reactance* and there is both *capacitive reactance* and *inductive reactance*. A circuit invariably contains resistance in addition to either or both of these so we will also need to rate the various combinations of reactance and resistance, again with Ohm's Law still effective. Such a combination is known as the *impedance* of a circuit, and with regard to this we must also deal with the additional complication of phase angles for which we are already prepared by our studies of the use of phasors.

3.1 REACTANCE

To get to grips with the concept of reactance we first study it in circuits uncomplicated by the presence of resistance. Capacitive reactance is treated at length first, followed by inductive reactance in a somewhat reduced form to avoid duplication of the many principles involved which are similar. There is no significance in the order in which the two types of reactance are discussed.

3.1.1 Capacitive Reactance

So that Ohm's Law can be used equally in an alternating current circuit containing capacitance as in a direct current circuit with resistance, we must find what constitutes reactance so that

$$I = \frac{V}{X_C}$$

where I and V are current through and voltage across a capacitor C, and X_C is its reactance.

We do not consider resistance at this stage, the practical circuit with its inevitable resistance follows later.

The definition of the Coulomb helps recall of the formula for the quantity of charge in a capacitor as

$$Q = i \times t,$$

one coulomb being the charge arising from a current (i) of one ampere flowing for a time (t) of one second. Since

$$i = \frac{Q}{t},$$

then i can be considered as being equal to the rate of charge (or discharge) at any instant in coulombs per second. We now change to the lower case q because we are interested more in instantaneous, small values. Also we use the more convention-al mathematical way of expressing rate of change of one quantity with another[A4.3] thus

$$i = \frac{dq}{dt}$$

and since at any instant

$$q = C \times v$$

(where v is the instantaneous voltage across the capacitor) then for a fixed capacitance C, the rate of charge is equal to the rate of change of voltage. Put in a slightly different way, the voltage across the capacitor increases at the same rate as the charge flowing into it — not too difficult to appreciate when we recall that charge is due to the build-up of electrons on one set of plates with a corresponding loss from the other set and that the voltage is simply a measure of the difference in charge on the two sets of plates.

Then

$$\frac{dq}{dt} = \frac{dv}{dt} \times C$$

and since

$$i = \frac{dq}{dt}, \qquad \frac{dv}{dt} = \frac{i}{C}$$

Now for a sinusoidal current,

$$i = I_m \sin \omega t$$

∴

$$\frac{dv}{dt} = \frac{I_m \sin \omega t}{C} \qquad (1)$$

This equation holds for instantaneous values but we are not seeking a formula for instantaneous reactance but one for the reactance to a whole cycle of a waveform. The latter can be obtained by considering a quarter-cycle only since the average value of the waveform as it rises or falls between 0 and E_m is the same for each quarter.

The time for a quarter-cycle is 1/4f where f is the frequency of the applied waveform.

∴ Average rate of change of voltage is

$$\frac{E_m - 0}{1/4f} = 4f\,E_m \quad (= \text{average of } dv/dt)$$

and taking the average value of both sides of equation (1) (Section 1.3.2)

$$4f\, E_m = \frac{(2/\pi) \times I_m}{C}$$

$$\therefore \quad \frac{E_m}{I_m} = \frac{2}{\pi \times C \times 4f} = \frac{1}{2\pi fC}$$

But we are intending to call the ratio of E_m/I_m, X_C

$\therefore X_C$ (the reactance of a capacitor) is

$$\frac{1}{2\pi fC} \quad \text{or} \quad \frac{1}{\omega C} \quad \text{ohms}$$

that is, a circuit or capacitor has a capacitive reactance of one ohm when an alternating current of one ampere produces an alternating voltage of one volt across it. The current and voltage are rms (effective) values. From the formula, as C or f increase, X_C falls and unlike resistors a capacitor cannot be marked with its reactance because this depends on the frequency of the waveform applied to it.

Returning to the relationship

$$\frac{dv}{dt} = \frac{i}{C} \, ,$$

because C is constant, the instantaneous current through a capacitor is related to the rate of change of voltage across it at that instant, not to the magnitude of the voltage as is the case with a resistor. We can examine this further by plotting a graph of voltage and then current based on the rate of change of voltage. Let us take, say, $18°$ steps as in Table 3.1 of a typical voltage waveform of $E_m = 1$ V, f = 100 Hz. The waveform period is then $1/100$ s $= 0.01$ s, $18°$ being equivalent to $18/360 \times 0.01$ s $= 0.5$ ms. (For this investigation, disregard the bottom section of the table.)

CAPACITIVE REACTANCE $e = E_m \sin \phi$, $f = 100$ Hz				
$\angle \phi^\circ$ (1)	$\sin \phi$ (2)	v ($= E_m \sin \phi$) volts (3)	Rise in v over 18° volts (4)	Rate of change of v over 18° volts/sec (5)
0	0	0		
18	0.3090	0.3090	0.3090	618.0
36	0.5878	0.5878	0.2788	557.6
54	0.8090	0.8090	0.2212	442.4
72	0.9511	0.9511	0.1421	284.2
90	1.0000	1.0000	0.0489	97.8
108	0.9511	0.9511	−0.0489	−97.8
$\angle \phi^\circ$ (1)	$\sin \phi$ (2)	i ($= I_m \sin \phi$) amps (3)	Rise in i over 18° amps (4)	Rate of change of i over 18° amps/sec (5)
INDUCTIVE REACTANCE $i = I_m \sin \phi$, $f = 100$ Hz				

TABLE 3.1 Calculation of voltage and current and their rate of change in reactive circuits

Fig. 3.1 shows the results from Cols. 3 and 5 of the table plotted against the angle through which the capacitor voltage v has moved. The rate of change is plotted at the middle of each 18° interval. The Col. 3 graph is labelled "v (capacitive)" and the Col. 5 labelled "i (capacitive)". Note that the latter is not truly a graph of i but predicts the shape and phase of it. It is only necessary to plot over one quarter of a cycle because from our experience, the remainder of the cycle comprises the same shaped curves in their different positions. The waveform

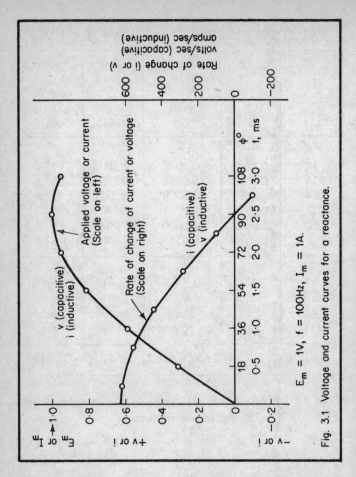

Fig. 3.1 Voltage and current curves for a reactance.

$E_m = 1V$, $f = 100Hz$, $I_m = 1A$.

for i is clearly 90° in advance of that for v for its positive peak occurs on the graph at 0° whereas that for v follows at 90° (2.5 ms later), so for a capacitor the current leads the voltage by 90° ($\pi/2$ radians). This is independent of the actual value of C for it has not entered our calculations at all.

This surprising result, for it seems that when a voltage is applied to a capacitor, the current it causes actually gets there beforehand, is explained by the fact that the charge (and discharge) currents of a capacitor commence at the maximum value even though the voltage applied is extremely small. As the latter builds up, the charge increases and opposes further current flow, the current consequently falls. This feature also helps to give credence to the fact determined above that as frequency rises, capacitive reactance falls. Consider first a low frequency, the period is long and the capacitor has more time to charge or discharge during each half-cycle. For a high frequency the period is short and the charge built up before reversal of the applied waveform is small. Because the capacitor current commences at maximum (i_1) then progressively falls during each half-cycle (to i_2) it is clear that the average current $((i_1 - i_2)/2)$ during the half-cycle must be less for the longer period, by Ohm's Law a lower average current implies a higher reactance.

We are now confronted not only with reactance but also with the fact that voltage and current are not in phase. When one is maximum the other is zero and vice versa so we look like being in trouble in trying to calculate the power from V x I. In fact, no power can be expended in a pure reactance and this fact will be appreciated more as we progress. Phasors help with the difficulty of visualizing conditions in a circuit when there are time differences so let us represent the two waveforms of Fig. 3.1 on a phasor diagram, remembering that the latter is simply a device for seeing the picture without the need for drawing a graph.

Suppose C = 1 μF, we know that $v = E_m \sin \phi$ and we can now calculate X_C for

$$X_C = \frac{1}{2\pi fC} = \frac{1}{2\pi \times 100 \times 1 \times 10^{-6}} = \frac{10^4}{2\pi} \, \Omega$$

Then
$$I_m = \frac{E_m}{X_C} = \frac{1}{X_C} = \frac{2\pi}{10^4} A = \frac{2\pi}{10} \, mA = 0.6283 \, mA$$

In this case there is no need to convert to rms values (Section

1.3.3) because the multiplying factor is the same for both voltage and current, but we do so for practice. The subscript m (for maximum) on E or I is dropped when rms values are used,

$$E = \frac{E_m}{\sqrt{2}}, \quad I = \frac{I_m}{\sqrt{2}}$$

$$\therefore \quad E = 0.707 \text{ V} \quad I = \frac{0.6283}{\sqrt{2}} = 0.444 \text{ mA}$$

The phasor diagrams are shown in Fig. 3.2. There is a choice as to whether the voltage or the current is chosen as the reference (3 o'clock) phasor, in diagram (i) it is v_c, in diagram (ii) i. In both cases i leads v_c by 90°. This is all the diagrams show us, there is no further work to be done because the circuit is of simplest form when it contains pure capacitance only, that is, only the current can be calculated for a given frequency, the phase angle already being known.

Note that an alternating current does not flow *through* a capacitor, the current in the circuit is due to the alternate charging and discharging.

EXAMPLE:
A capacitor of 1.27 μF and negligible resistance is connected to a 250 V (rms), 50 Hz mains supply. What current flows?

$$V = 250 \text{ V} \quad f = 50 \text{ Hz} \quad I = ?$$

$$X_C = \frac{1}{2\pi fC} = \frac{1}{100\pi \times 1.27 \times 10^{-6}} = \frac{10^4}{1.27\pi} \approx 2500 \ \Omega$$

$$\therefore \text{Current,} \quad I = \frac{V}{X_C} = \frac{250}{2500} \text{ A} = \underline{100 \text{ mA}}$$

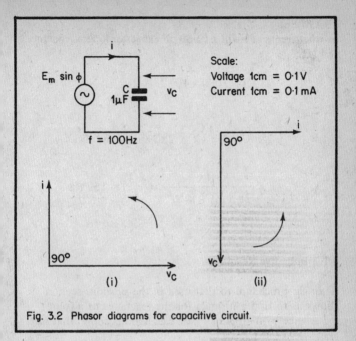

Fig. 3.2 Phasor diagrams for capacitive circuit.

EXAMPLE:
What is the reactance of a 68 pF capacitor at 100 kHz and at
1 MHz?

$$C = 68 \times 10^{-12} \text{ F}$$

At 100 kHz,

$$X_C = \frac{1}{2\pi \times 10^5 \times 68 \times 10^{-12}} = \frac{10^7}{2\pi \times 68} = \underline{23,405 \ \Omega}$$

At 1 MHz,

$$X_C = \frac{1}{2\pi \times 10^6 \times 68 \times 10^{-12}} = \frac{10^6}{2\pi \times 68} = \underline{2,340.5 \ \Omega}$$

But clearly in the second case, since the frequency is higher by
10 times, all that is needed is to divide the first answer by 10.

EXAMPLE:
At what frequency will a 1,000 pF capacitor have a reactance of 1 MΩ?

$$C = 1000 \times 10^{-12} = 10^{-9} \text{ F}$$

$$X_C = \frac{1}{2\pi fC} \quad \therefore fX_C = \frac{1}{2\pi C} \quad \therefore f = \frac{1}{2\pi C \cdot X_C}$$

$$\therefore \quad f = \frac{1}{2\pi \times 10^{-9} \times 10^{6}} = \frac{10^{3}}{2\pi} = \underline{159 \text{ Hz}}$$

3.1.2 Inductive Reactance

A similar procedure to that used in the previous section allows us to find a formula for the reactance of a (pure) inductance so that Ohm's Law calculations apply, that is,

$$I = \frac{V}{X_L}$$

where I and V are current through and voltage across an inductor L, and X_L is its reactance.

The definition of inductance has already been shown to be one henry if an emf of one volt is induced when the current changes uniformly at one ampere per second, from which

$$e = L \times \text{rate of change of current, i.e.} \quad \frac{L(i_2 - i_1)}{t}$$

or using the mathematical expression for rate of change of current with time,

$$e = L \frac{di}{dt}$$

$$\therefore \quad L \frac{di}{dt} = E_m \sin \omega t \quad \text{or} \quad \frac{di}{dt} = \frac{E_m \sin \omega t}{L} \quad (2)$$

To find the reactance to the whole cycle of an applied wave-form we have again to consider its average value which is conveniently calculated over one quarter of a cycle, of time $1/4f$ where f is the frequency of the applied waveform.

Since in a pure inductance the current rises uniformly (remember, this is a theoretical consideration only) then

$$\text{Average rate of change of current} = \frac{I_m - 0}{1/4f} = 4fI_m$$

(= average of di/dt) and taking the average value of both sides of equation (2),

$$4fI_m = \frac{2/\pi \times E_m}{L}$$

$$\therefore \quad \frac{E_m}{I_m} = 4fL \times \frac{\pi}{2} = 2\pi fL$$

and since we intend calling the ratio E_m/I_m the reactance X_L, then

$$X_L = \underline{2\pi fL \text{ or } \omega L \text{ ohms}},$$

that is, a circuit or inductor has an inductive reactance of one ohm when an alternating current of one ampere produces an alternating voltage of one volt across it. The current and voltage are rms (effective) values. From the formula, as L or f increase, X_L increases.

Returning to the relationship

$$\frac{di}{dt} = \frac{e}{L},$$

as L is constant, the instantaneous voltage across an inductance is related to the rate of change of current through it at that instant. If we now follow the same technique as for a capacitor to determine the relative phases of voltage and current in an inductive circuit we shall find that by considering a current $i = I_m \sin \phi$ to flow where $I_m = 1$ ampere, Table 3.1 applies but with new column titles as shown at the bottom. Col. 3 produces the curve in Fig. 3.1 marked "i (inductive)" and Col. 5 gives "v (inductive)". Compared with capacitive reactance the phase position is reversed for v leads i, that is, for an inductor the current lags on the voltage by $90°$ ($\pi/2$ radians).

The remarks in the previous section which follow the discussion on Fig. 3.1 also apply in the case of inductive reactance with suitable and obvious amendments, for example, by Ohm's Law a lower average current implies a higher reactance, also the fact that no power can be expended in a purely inductive reactance. There is also little gain in including another figure similar to Fig. 3.2 to show the phasor diagrams for an inductive circuit since we can now appreciate how these are drawn, that is, with v_L leading i by $90°$. Such phasor diagrams will be part of more complex ones which follow.

The following examples involve theoretical considerations only for in practice, even more so than in the case of a capacitor, resistance is present with inductance.

EXAMPLE:
An inductor of 2 H is used on a 60 Hz mains supply. What is its reactance?

$$L = 2\,H, \quad f = 60\,Hz$$

then,
$$X_L = 2\pi fL = 2\pi \times 60 \times 2 = \underline{754 \ \Omega}$$

EXAMPLE:
What value of inductor will have a reactance of 1000 Ω on a 50 Hz supply?

$$X_L = 1000 \ \Omega, \quad f = 50 \ Hz$$

then,
$$X_L = 2\pi fL \quad \therefore L = \frac{X_L}{2\pi f} = \frac{1000}{2\pi \times 50} = \underline{3.18 \ H}$$

EXAMPLE:
What is the reactance of an inductor of 31.83 μH at 50 and 100 MHz?

$$L = 31.83 \ \mu H = 31.83 \times 10^{-6} \ H$$

$$f_1 = 50 \ MHz = 50 \times 10^6 \ Hz$$

then,
$$X_L \text{ at } 50 \text{ MHz} = 2\pi f_1 L = 2\pi \times 50 \times 10^6 \times 31.83 \times 10^{-6}$$

$$= \underline{10,000 \ \Omega}$$

$$X_L \text{ at } 100 \text{ MHz} = 2 \times (X_L \text{ at } 50 \text{ MHz}) = \underline{20,000 \ \Omega}$$

EXAMPLE:
At what frequency will a 0.1 H inductor have a reactance of 400π ohms?

$$X_L = 400\pi \ \Omega \quad L = 0.1 \ H$$

then,
$$X_L = 2\pi fL \quad \therefore f = \frac{X_L}{2\pi L} = \frac{400\pi}{2\pi \times 0.1} = \underline{2000 \ Hz}$$

3.1.3 Summary of Ohm's Law applied to simple AC circuits

In the preceding two sections we talked in terms of voltage and current being out of phase by 90° in pure reactances. Considering a current i as a reference phasor as in Fig. 3.2 (ii), for a capacitance the voltage v_C lags on i by 90°, conversely for an inductance the voltage v_L leads by 90°.

Capacitive reactance is given by

$$X_C = \frac{V_C}{I_C} \quad (V_C \text{ lags on } I_C \text{ by } 90°)$$

but from Section 1.3.4 this could be expressed more simply in complex notation as $-jV_C/I_C$, the $-j$ taking the place of the statement on phase within the brackets. So in effect capacitive reactance is completely expressed by

$$X_C = \frac{-j}{\omega C} \quad \text{or} \quad \frac{-j}{2\pi f C}$$

Similarly because for inductive reactance V_L leads I_L by 90°, it is completely expressed by

$$X_L = j\omega L \quad \text{or} \quad j2\pi f L$$

Generally therefore capacitive reactance is regarded as being negative and inductive reactance as positive.

Summarizing therefore:

Resistance: $\quad I_R = \dfrac{V_R}{R} \qquad (I_R \text{ and } V_R \text{ are in phase})$

Capacitance: $\quad I_C = \dfrac{V_C}{X_C} = \dfrac{V_C}{-j/\omega C} = \dfrac{V_C \cdot \omega C}{-j} = jV_C \cdot \omega C$

Inductance: $$I_L = \frac{V_L}{X_L} = \frac{V_L}{j\omega L} = \frac{-jV_L}{\omega L}$$

(remembering that $j \times j = -1$ and $j \times -j = +1$).

It might at first be thought that the signs have ended up the wrong way round but taking capacitance as an example, if V_C is made the reference phasor, then the current phasor has a magnitude of $V_C \omega C$ multiplied by j, that is, rotated into a $90°$ lead. Similarly if V_L is made the reference phasor for an inductance, I_L has a magnitude of $V_L/\omega L$ rotated into a $90°$ lag ($-j$).

3.2   IMPEDANCE

In a given circuit, whatever mixture of resistance and reactance exists, it remains constant, hence when a sinusoidal voltage is applied, it results in a certain sinusoidal current flow. There is therefore for that circuit a fixed ratio of voltage to current so again we can produce an Ohm's Law for a mixed circuit just as has been done separately for purely resistive and purely reactive ones. For these there are R and X which when properly defined state the opposition to current flow in accordance with the law. Now there must be one more term for the opposition to current flow in a circuit neither purely resistive nor purely reactive, but a combination of the two. The term is *Impedance*, generally known by a capital Z with subscripts as required. Hence

$$Z \text{ (ohms)} = \frac{V \text{ (volts)}}{I \text{ (amps)}},$$

V and I usually being expressed in rms values.

There are no phase angle considerations with resistance and only $\pm 90°$ for pure reactance, but for the combination it is now apparent that there will be some angle between $+90°$ and

$-90°$. We need to look at this generally before getting down to detail with the various practical resistive and reactive combinations which are possible.

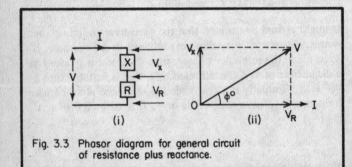

Fig. 3.3 Phasor diagram for general circuit
of resistance plus reactance.

Suppose a circuit comprises resistive and reactive components in series and a voltage V drives a current I through them as shown in Fig. 3.3 (i). We know that the voltages V_X and V_R add up to make V and this is where phasor diagrams enter the scene. In Fig. 3.3 the current I which is the common feature, is first drawn as the reference phasor OI. On the same line is drawn OV_R to represent the voltage V_R (= IR) and then V_X (= IX) at right angles to represent the reactive voltage, leading V_R by $90°$. We could just as effectively have shown V_X lagging by $90°$, but this in no way affects the conclusion. Now, because this is a phasor diagram, V can be obtained from the diagonal after completion of the rectangle as developed in Section 1.3.4. For revision of this section let us recall what the diagram tells us:

(i) V_R is on the real axis, V_X on the imaginary. V_R and V_X are rectangular coordinates.

(ii) V is the resultant of V_R and V_X which are $90°$ out of phase (in quadrature).

(iii) V leads I (and V_R) by an angle $\phi°$ which is less than $90°$.

104

(iv) In polar form, $V = \sqrt{V_R{}^2 + V_X{}^2} \ . \ \tan^{-1} V_X/V_R$
(modulus and angle).

(v) In complex notation $V = V_R + jV_X$.

Now from (v) by dividing both sides of the equation by I,

$$\frac{V}{I} = \frac{V_R}{I} + j \frac{V_X}{I}$$

and therefore by Ohm's Law for each term

$$Z = R + jX$$

This is an important conclusion but one which can easily lead to confusion if we do not remove uncertainties first. It has been shown continually that a phasor diagram is a device to show pictorially and with greater simplicity than a graph, the phase relationship between two separate sinusoidal quantities. Now $R + jX$ means that R and X have a 90° phase difference, but how can a fixed quantity such as an impedance have two components with a phase or time difference between them? Of course it cannot. So we do not use phasor diagrams with impedances. However we do need a way of showing how an impedance will treat the voltage and current presented to it, for example, is it mostly reactive, that is, has a large angle and causes the voltage to be well out of phase with the current or vice versa? A mere statement that the impedance is x ohms does not tell us this, hence it is also necessary to quote the phase angle it would impart on, for example, the resultant voltage relative to the reference current. This is demonstrated as follows:

The impedance Z which in complex notation is given by $R + jX$ is also given in polar coordinates as $|Z| \angle \phi°$. By Ohm's Law, the voltage V is therefore $I \times Z$, i.e. $|I| \angle 0° \times |Z| \angle \phi°$ when both I and Z are split up into their moduli and angles.

Now, as shown in Section 1.3.4, to multiply two quantities

in polar form, we multiply the moduli but add the angles:

$$\therefore \qquad V = |I| \times |Z| \angle \phi^{\circ}$$

which shows that the angle of the impedance has been impressed on the voltage.

Thus by quoting the impedance as either $Z = R + jX$ or $Z = |Z| \angle \phi$ we have the complete picture as in Fig. 3.4. Although technically we cannot use phasor diagrams with impedance for the reasons given above, we can avoid being incorrect by calling them *impedance diagrams* embodying vectors[A4.1] rather than phasors. But we must not mix the two types of diagram.

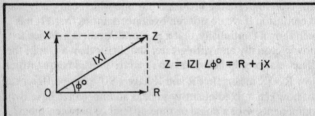

Fig. 3.4 Impedance diagram.

The sections following will give plenty of experience with these principles.

3.3 POWER

Section 1.3.3 demonstrates that by using rms values for sinusoidal current and voltage, their product automatically gives the power in an ac circuit, provided that the latter is resistive, that is, no phase angle exists. This is one good reason for the use of rms values. $V \times I$ gives what is known as the *true power* in a circuit, i.e.

$$P \text{ (watts)} = V \text{ (volts, rms)} \times I \text{ (amps, rms)} = I^2 R = \frac{V^2}{R}$$

where R is the circuit resistance.

For a completely reactive circuit however, it has already been mentioned that no power can be dissipated, hence in this section it is now right that we should prove and understand this fact. All we have to do is to calculate a range of instantaneous values of v and i throughout a complete cycle, multiply each pair together to obtain the instantaneous power values and finally total these over the cycle. We shall find that it is immaterial whether we examine capacitive or inductive reactance, the conclusions will be the same, let us choose inductive reactance to avoid one extra minus sign.

For a purely inductive circuit, the voltage leads the current by $90°$, therefore if

$$i = I_m \sin \omega t ,$$

$$v = V_m \sin (\omega t + \pi/2).$$

For convenience, let both I_m and $V_m = 1$. A table for calculating the graph points might be as shown in Table 3.2, the results of which are plotted in Fig. 3.5 (i). The curve for power is seen to be sinusoidal but to have double the frequency of the current and voltage. The shaded area between the power curve and the horizontal axis may be taken to represent the energy involved and here we must take account of signs. Areas above the horizontal axis are classed as representing positive energy, that is, energy from the supply (in the form of the current) to set up a magnetic field around the inductor windings. "Negative energy" arises when the magnetic field collapses and by virtue of the induced emf in the windings, returns that energy to the supply. With a capacitor the same type of energy transfer takes place through the continual charging and discharging. Because the positive and negative pulses of energy are equal over each complete cycle, none is taken from the supply, that is, the power expended in a purely reactive circuit is zero.

If we now consider a partly resistive and partly reactive circuit

107

ωt (rads)	Equivalent angle in degrees	$\sin \omega t$ (gives i, amps)	$(\omega t + \pi/2)$ (rads)	Equivalent angle in degrees	$\sin(\omega t + \pi/2)$ (gives v, volts)	$p = v \times i$ (watts)
0	0	0	0.5π	90	1.0	0
0.083π	15	0.2588	0.583π	105	0.9659	0.2500
0.167π	30	0.5000	0.667π	120	0.8660	0.4330
0.250π	45	0.7071	0.750π	135	0.7071	0.5000
0.333π	60	0.8660	0.833π	150	0.5000	0.4330
0.417π	75	0.9659	0.917π	165	0.2588	0.2500
0.500π	90	1.0000	1.000π	180	0	0
0.583π	105	0.9659	1.083π	195	−0.2588	−0.2500
.....	.....	.....	.....	.....	.....	......

TABLE 3.2 Calculation of instantaneous power in a purely reactive circuit

108

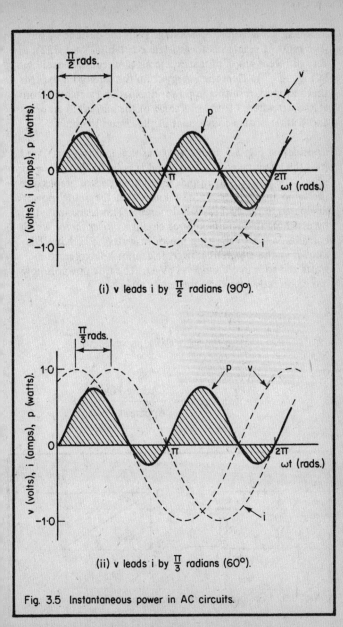

(i) v leads i by $\frac{\Pi}{2}$ radians (90°).

(ii) v leads i by $\frac{\Pi}{3}$ radians (60°).

Fig. 3.5 Instantaneous power in AC circuits.

in which, for example, the voltage leads the current by 60° (the ratio of reactance to resistance is tan 60° = 1.732), a very different graph of instantaneous power results as shown in Fig. 3.5 (ii). Here the energy from the supply far exceeds that returned, resulting in power dissipation calculated from I^2R watts where I is the rms value of the current in amperes and R the resistive component of the circuit in ohms.

Considering Fig. 3.5 again, it is clear that multiplying V by I (not the instantaneous values v and i) as with Ohm's Law to obtain the power is incorrect, for the two sets of graphs give the same answer, yet we now know that the actual power dissipated in the two cases is different. This is accounted for by assigning to a component or circuit a *power factor* which converts V x I to the true power in watts. V x I itself is known as the *apparent power*, it cannot be expressed in watts and so is in *voltamperes* (VA). The true power is now more correctly known as the *active power*.

Then

$$\text{Active Power} = VI \times \text{power factor}$$

or

$$\text{power factor} = \frac{\text{Active Power}}{\text{Apparent Power}}$$

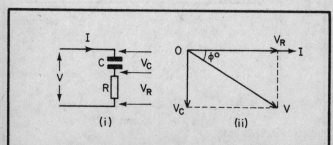

Fig. 3.6 Resistance and capacitance in series.

Consider any resistive/reactive circuit such as Fig. 3.6 (i), the average power dissipated must be equal to $I^2 R$ watts. The apparent power is VI voltamperes:

$$\therefore \qquad I^2 R = VI \times \text{power factor}$$

i.e

$$\text{power factor} = \frac{I^2 R}{VI} = \frac{IR}{V}$$

But $IR = V_R$ and from Fig. 3.6 (ii), $V_R = V \cos \phi$.

$$\therefore \qquad \text{power factor} = \frac{V_R}{V} = \frac{V \cos \phi}{V} = \underline{\cos \phi} \; .$$

$\cos \phi$ is simply a ratio and therefore is not expressed in any units. Also the impedance Z of the circuit is given by V/I,

$$\therefore \qquad \frac{I}{V} = \frac{1}{Z}$$

$\therefore$ since power factor $= IR/V$, it is also equal to $\underline{R/Z}$ and the average power in any circuit containing reactance is generally expressed as $VI \cos \phi$. The power factor has values from 0 to 1.

EXAMPLE:
An inductor has a self-inductance of 138 mH and a resistance of 30 Ω. What is its power factor and what power will it draw from a 120 V, 60 Hz supply?

$$L = 138 \, \text{mH} = 0.138 \, \text{H} ,$$

$$R = 30 \, \Omega , \qquad V = 120 \, \text{V} , \qquad f = 60 \, \text{Hz}$$

Inductive Reactance,

$$X_L = 2\pi f L = 2\pi \times 60 \times 0.138 = 52 \, \Omega$$

Impedance,
$$Z = \sqrt{R^2 + X_L^2} = \sqrt{30^2 + 52^2} = 60 \ \Omega$$

Then,
$$I = \frac{V}{Z} = \frac{120}{60} = 2 \ A$$

$\phi = \tan^{-1} X_L/R$ (check with Fig. 3.4 if necessary) =

$$\tan^{-1} \frac{52}{30} = 60°$$

∴   Power Factor $= \cos \phi = \cos 60° = \underline{0.5}$

and
  Power Dissipated $= VI \cos \phi = 120 \times 2 \times 0.5 = \underline{120 \ \text{watts}}$

3.4   Q-FACTOR

We shall appreciate more and more as we progress that in many circuits resistance is detrimental to efficiency. A typical example (explained further in a later section) is that of a *tuning circuit*, that is, one which is capable of accepting a particular band of frequencies while rejecting all others. It is used in radio receivers where a particular radio station is *tuned in*. In the tuning circuits themselves resistance impairs the *sharpness* of tuning and the engineer needs some way of describing the goodness or superiority of a component or circuit for this purpose. Reactance is required, too much resistance is not because it causes power losses therefore an obvious measure is the ratio of one to the other, i.e. X/R. This ratio is termed the *quality factor* or more generally the *Q-factor*, often just plain "Q". Generally we refer to the Q of a capacitor, inductor or circuit. Other formulae will be found to express Q but the one with which we are concerned at present is simply

$$Q = \frac{X}{R},$$

thus for a capacitor

$$Q = \frac{(1/\omega C)}{R} = \frac{1}{\omega CR}$$

and for an inductor

$$\frac{\omega L}{R}$$

If R is constant with frequency (and this may not necessarily be so) then Q is not constant for any particular case but itself varies with frequency.

The inherent resistance of the modern capacitor is sufficiently low compared with its reactance at working frequencies that Q is seldom used as a measure of quality. The opposite applies in the case of an inductor.

3.5 SERIES CIRCUITS

Drawing a phasor diagram involves first the choice of the reference phasor, for voltage or current. With a series circuit, the current is the natural choice because it is exactly the same throughout the circuit, for if it were not there would be a build-up of charge somewhere, creating voltages not in agreement with Ohm's Law.

3.5.1 Resistance and Capacitance

The circuit of Fig. 3.6 (i) results in the phasor diagram of (ii). As above, the current I is made the reference (OI). V_R is in phase with I and therefore its phasor OV_R is drawn along the reference line. (In Fig. 3.6 (ii) OI is shown as being longer than OV_R, it could equally be shorter, this simply depends on the relative scales chosen). V_C lags on I by 90° giving the phasor OV_C. The resultant is OV representing the applied voltage V shown to be lagging on the current by ϕ°

This is a general diagram, the actual lengths of the phasors cannot be determined unless the frequency is known and the reactance of the capacitor calculated. Let us illustrate this in a practical way:

Consider the series circuit of Fig. 3.7 (iv) and assume V to be maintained at 100 V but at the frequencies shown in the

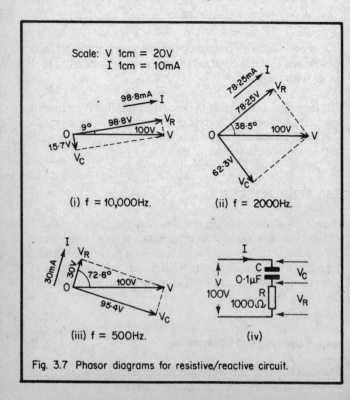

Fig. 3.7 Phasor diagrams for resistive/reactive circuit.

114

diagrams (i) to (iii). This is a slightly exceptional case where for the sake of comparison the constant factor is made V, while I varies from diagram to diagram. Thus although this is a series circuit, for this purpose we make V the reference. For convenience R has been chosen as 1000 Ω so that V_R in volts and I in mA may have the same length phasors. We know V, C, R and f and wish to see how V_R, V_C, I and their relative phases vary with frequency. First calculate for diagram (i):

$$f = 10,000 \text{ Hz}, \qquad C = 0.1 \ \mu\text{F}$$

$$\therefore X_C = \frac{1}{2\pi fC} = \frac{1}{2\pi \times 10^4 \times 0.1 \times 10^{-6}} = \frac{10^3}{2\pi} = 159.15 \ \Omega$$

and this is given a negative sign because it is capacitive (Section 3.1.3).

To calculate I we first need the impedance Z $(= |Z| \angle \phi°)$

$$|Z| = \sqrt{R^2 + X_C^2} = \sqrt{1000^2 + (-159.15)^2} = 1012.6 \ \Omega$$

$$\phi = \tan^{-1} \frac{X_C}{R} = \tan^{-1} \frac{159.15}{1000} = \tan^{-1} -0.15916 = -9°$$

By Ohm's Law

$$I = \frac{V}{Z} = \frac{100 \angle 0°}{1012.6 \angle -9°} = \frac{100}{1012.6} \underline{/0 - (-9)°} \text{ amps} =$$

$$= 98.76 \angle 9° \text{ mA}$$

showing that I has an angle of +9° relative to V which itself has an angle of 0° because we made it so.

Then

$$V_R = |I| \times R = \frac{98.76}{1000} \times 1000 = 98.76 \text{ V}$$

which we know to be in phase with I

$$V_C = |I| \times X_C = \frac{98.76}{1000} \times 159.15 = 15.72 \text{ V}$$

which we know to be lagging by 90° on I.

The phasor diagram can be drawn as in (i), similarly for f = 2000 Hz and 500 Hz as in (ii) and (iii).

What we learn from this particular example is that as frequency falls and therefore X_C increases, V_C increases and V_R falls while the circuit current becomes more out-of-phase with the applied voltage. This is to be expected for at the extremes a purely resistive circuit has a phase angle between V and I of 0° whereas for a purely reactive circuit it is 90°. For an angle of 45°, since tan 45° = 1 (= V_C/V_R), V_C and V_R are equal.

As a point of practical interest note that as f increases from 500 Hz to 10,000 Hz, V_C falls from 95.4 V to 15.7 V. This is the principle of an audio system *tone control* to cut down the output of the system at the higher (treble) frequencies, for if the voltage V_C is used to drive the amplifier feeding the loudspeaker, the output at the higher frequencies will be reduced.

Careful study of these diagrams with some vision as to what they are trying to tell us about the relative positions of the sine waves themselves on a graph helps in appreciation of the basic complexity of the ac circuit. Once this is clearly established in the mind, alternating current theory should no longer give rise to anxiety.

3.5.2 Resistance and Inductance

The presence of only a very small amount of resistance in a capacitor usually enables us to carry out calculations with this ignored. Not so with an inductor, for by the very nature of its construction of a coil of wire, it must have built into it at least the resistance of the wire. Furthermore, as we shall see later, at the higher frequencies the resistance increases above its dc value. These complications need not worry us yet because in this section we are dealing exclusively with series circuits and the inductor itself can be represented by a pure inductance in series with its total effective resistance so we fit it in by simply adding the resistance to the remaining circuit resistance. (An inductor can also be represented by a pure inductance in parallel with a different value of resistance – it all depends on the method used for measurement.)

Fig. 3.8 (ii) shows the general phasor diagram for the circuit in (i). The current is common to all components, hence is used as the reference and in phase with it, end to end, are V_r and V_R as shown. V_L leads I by $90°$ giving V, the applied voltage leading I by the angle $\phi°$. An example on calculation of the impedance of an inductor is given at the end of Section 3.3.

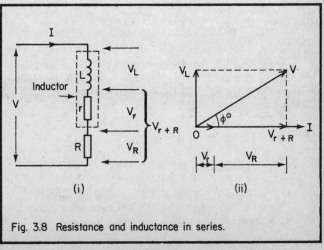

Fig. 3.8 Resistance and inductance in series.

117

EXAMPLE:
An inductor of value 37.3 mH has a (series) resistance of 35 Ω. 50 V is maintained across it at 400 Hz. Determine (i) the impedance of the inductor, (ii) the current and its phase angle relative to the voltage, (iii) the power-factor, (iv) the Q-factor, (v) the voltage across the resistive and reactive components. Check that the latter add up to the applied voltage.

$$L = 37.3 \text{ mH} = 0.0373 \text{ H} ,$$

$$R = 35 \, \Omega , \quad V = 50 \text{ V} , \quad f = 400 \text{ Hz}$$

(i) $X_L = 2\pi f L = 2\pi \times 400 \times 0.0373 = 93.7 \, \Omega$, then

$$|Z| = \sqrt{R^2 + X_L^2} = \sqrt{35^2 + 93.7^2} = \sqrt{10004.7} = 100 \, \Omega$$

$$\phi = \tan^{-1} \frac{X_L}{R} = \tan^{-1} \frac{93.7}{35} = \tan^{-1} 2.677 = 69.5°$$

$$(X_L \text{ is positive})$$

i.e. Impedance = 100 Ω $\angle 69.5°$.

(ii) $I = \dfrac{V}{Z} = \dfrac{50 \angle 0°}{100 \angle 69.5°} = 0.5 \text{ A} \angle -69.5°$

(the calculation of the angle is included for completeness, but it could be predicted instead from the angle of the impedance), i.e. a current of 0.5 A flows lagging on the voltage by 69.5°.

(iii) Power-factor = $\cos \phi = \cos 69.5° = 0.35.$

(iv) Q = $\omega L/R$ (i.e. X_L/R) = 93.7/35 = 2.68.

(v) $V_R = IR = 0.5 \times 35 = 17.5$ V (in phase with I)

$$V_L = IX_L = 0.5 \times 93.7 = 46.85 \text{ V} \ (90° \text{ ahead of I}).$$

V_R and V_L must be added "vectorially", i.e.

$$V = \sqrt{V_R^2 + V_L^2} = \sqrt{17.5^2 + 46.85^2} = \sqrt{2501} = 50 \text{ V}$$

A phasor diagram drawn to scale would give the same answer.

EXAMPLE:
Calculate the resistance of a 4 mH inductor which has an impedance of 1066 Ω at 30 kHz. What is the angle of the impedance and the Q?

$$L = 4 \text{ mH} = 4 \times 10^{-3} \text{ H}, \quad Z = 1066 \; \Omega,$$

$$f = 30 \times 10^3 \text{ Hz}$$

$$X_L = 2\pi f L = 2\pi \times 30 \times 10^3 \times 4 \times 10^{-3} = 754 \; \Omega$$

$$|Z| = \sqrt{R^2 + X_L^2} \; \therefore \; |Z|^2 = R^2 + X_L^2$$

$$\therefore \qquad R = \sqrt{|Z|^2 - X_L^2}$$

i.e. $\quad R = \sqrt{1066^2 - 754^2} = \sqrt{1136356 - 568516}$

$$= \sqrt{567840} = 754 \; \Omega$$

Thus R and X_L are equal, hence the angle of the impedance is 45° for

$$\tan^{-1} \frac{X_L}{R} = \tan^{-1} 1.0 = \underline{45°}$$

$$Q = \frac{X_L}{R} = \underline{1.0}$$

3.5.3 Resistance, Capacitance and Inductance

Mixing all three adds little complication to what we have already experienced because in the series circuit the voltages developed across the capacitive and inductive reactances are respectively lagging and leading the current by 90° so themselves are 180° out-of-phase. The lesser cancels out part of the greater, it being the latter which determines the net angle as being either +90° or −90°. Fig. 3.9 illustrates this where (i) is the circuit with R representing the total resistance and (ii) shows the phasor diagram with I and V_R drawn as before. Let us assume that component values and frequency are such that $X_L > X_C$ [A1], hence $V_L > V_C$. V_C cancels out part of V_L owing to the 180° phase difference and because the two phasors are in line V_C can be subtracted arithmetically from V_L leaving a net voltage ($V_L − V_C$), in this case leading the current as shown.

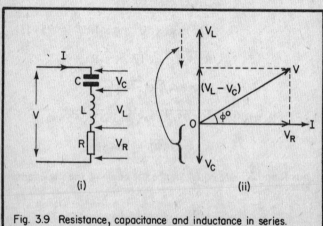

Fig. 3.9 Resistance, capacitance and inductance in series.

[Note: only when phasors are in line can their resultant be determined arithmetically, added when the arrows point in the same direction, subtracted when pointing in opposite directions. Apart from this, resultants are only obtained through completion of the parallelogram.]

The phasor for V follows by normal procedure. Thus, at this particular frequency the circuit is inductive, there is no evidence of capacitive reactance. From (ii)

$$V = \sqrt{V_R^2 + (V_L - V_C)^2} \quad \tan^{-1} \frac{(V_L - V_C)}{R}$$

Also, using complex notation, the imaginary quantity is $jV_L - jV_C$

$$\therefore \qquad V = V_R + jV_L - jV_C$$

and dividing throughout by I which is common to each term,

$$\frac{V}{I} = \frac{V_R}{I} + \frac{jV_L}{I} - \frac{jV_C}{I}$$

$$\therefore \qquad Z = R + jX_L - jX_C = R + j(X_L - X_C)$$

also $\qquad Z = \sqrt{R^2 + (X_L - X_C)^2} \quad \tan^{-1} \frac{(X_L - X_C)}{R}$

If $X_L > X_C$, the net reactance is inductive and V leads I, if $X_C > X_L$ the net reactance is capacitive and I leads V.

The formula for Z still holds good when $X_C > X_L$ for then $(X_L - X_C)$ gives the difference but with a negative sign, e.g. if $X_C = 90 \ \Omega$ and $X_L = 50 \ \Omega$ at a certain frequency, $(X_L - X_C) = 50 - 90 = -40\Omega$ thus indicating a net reactance of $40 \ \Omega$ which is capacitive. However, if we were to class capacitive reactance as negative from the start, the net reactance would be obtained from $(X_L + X_C)$. Both methods are equally valid and error is avoided as long as we check that the sign of the net reactance agrees with whichever of X_L or X_C is the greater.

EXAMPLE:
Calculate the impedance at 159.2 kHz of a series circuit consisting of L = 80 mH, C = 25 pF and total resistance R = 30 kΩ.

$$\omega = 2\pi f = 2\pi \times (159.2 \times 10^3) = 10^6 \ \text{rads/s}$$

121

$$X_L = \omega L = 10^6 \times 80 \times 10^{-3} = 8 \times 10^4 \ \Omega$$

$$X_C = \frac{1}{\omega C} = \frac{1}{10^6 \times 25 \times 10^{-12}} = \frac{10^6}{25} = \frac{100}{25} \times 10^4$$

$$= 4 \times 10^4 \ \Omega$$

$$(X_L - X_C) = 8 \times 10^4 - 4 \times 10^4 = 4 \times 10^4 \ \Omega$$

(positive because $X_L > X_C$), then

$$|Z| = \sqrt{R^2 + (X_L - X_C)^2} = \sqrt{(3 \times 10^4)^2 + (4 \times 10^4)^2}$$

$$= \sqrt{10^8(9 + 16)} = 5 \times 10^4 = 50 \ k\Omega$$

$$\phi = \tan^{-1} \frac{(X_L - X_C)}{R} = \tan^{-1} \frac{4 \times 10^4}{3 \times 10^4} = \tan^{-1} 1.333$$

$$= 53.1°$$

$\therefore$ Impedance of Circuit $= \underline{50 \ k\Omega \ \angle 53.1°}$

There was no reason to use complex algebra in this calculation because the answer could be obtained directly in polar notation. Complex notation could be used if required and the following example uses it with rationalization as explained in Section 1.3.4.

EXAMPLE:
An inductor of 207 mH and series resistance 4 Ω is connected in series with a capacitor of 39.8 μF and a resistor of 6 Ω to a 250 V 50 Hz supply. Calculate the current flowing.

$$\text{Total circuit resistance, } R = 4 + 6 = 10 \ \Omega$$

$$X_L = 2\pi f L = 2\pi \times 50 \times 0.207 = 65 \ \Omega$$

$$X_C = \frac{1}{2\pi fC} = \frac{1}{2\pi \times 50 \times 39.8 \times 10^{-6}} = \frac{10^6}{12500} = 80 \ \Omega$$

$$Z = R + j(X_L - X_C) = 10 + j65 - j80 = 10 - j15$$

$$I = \frac{V}{Z} = \frac{250}{10 - j15}$$

we cannot divide 250 by $10 - j15$ so we rationalize by multiplying numerator and denominator by the conjugate, $10 + j15$

$$\therefore \quad I = \frac{250}{10 - j15} \times \frac{10 + j15}{10 + j15} = \frac{2500 + j3750}{10^2 + 15^2}$$

$$= \frac{2500 + j3750}{325} = \underline{7.69 + j11.54 \text{ amps.}}$$

This is the value of the current in complex notation, the positive imaginary part showing that I leads V, which we would expect since the capacitive reactance exceeds the inductive, hence the circuit is capacitive (at 50 Hz).

In polar notation:

$$I = \sqrt{7.69^2 + 11.54^2} \quad \tan^{-1} \frac{11.54}{7.69}$$

$$= \sqrt{59.14 + 133.17} \quad \tan^{-1} 1.5 = 13.87 \angle 56.3° \text{ amps}$$

It is usually desirable to express the answer in polar notation because the modulus gives what would be read on a standard measuring instrument such as a voltmeter or ammeter. An ammeter connected in the above circuit would read 13.87 A, the phase angle is only given by more sophisticated measuring equipment, but fortunately for much work this is not required.

We can understand what actually occurs within the circuit from the fact that when an inductor and capacitor are interconnected with the same supply, the timing is such that as the magnetic field of the inductor begins to collapse and return energy to the circuit, the capacitor is ready to receive a charge from the circuit, hence in reality energy is transferred directly from inductor to capacitor.

Alternatively later in the cycle the discharging capacitor provides energy for the inductor to re-establish its magnetic field. There is thus an alternating transfer of energy between the two and because the energy required by one may be greater than that available from the other, the supply is affected to the extent of providing the difference.

3.6   PARALLEL CIRCUITS

In examining parallel ac circuits there is some danger of moving away too much from the "elements" of electronics towards the specialized. Thus parallel circuits are only considered briefly because of their greater complexity compared with series ones, for the latter are generally sufficient to instruct us in what we require in the main features of the ac circuit. However, there is no loss for the reader who wishes to develop expertise in this area because the techniques of analysis are no more than those already outlined. Accordingly a full analysis of the general parallel circuit of inductance and capacitance in parallel (both with their resistances) follows to demonstrate this and to act as a model for other circuits.

Consider Fig. 3. 10 (i). An inductor L and its associated resistance is connected in parallel with capacitor C also with its resistance. The combination has a voltage V applied. The main current I divides into currents I_L and I_C as shown.

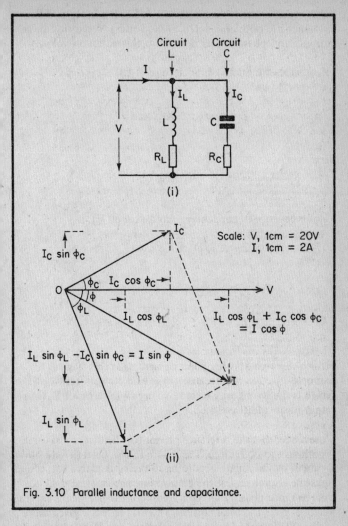

Scale: V, 1cm = 20V
I, 1cm = 2A

$I_C \sin \phi_C$

$I_C \cos \phi_C$

$I_L \cos \phi_L$

$I_L \cos \phi_L + I_C \cos \phi_C = I \cos \phi$

$I_L \sin \phi_L - I_C \sin \phi_C = I \sin \phi$

$I_L \sin \phi_L$

(ii)

Fig. 3.10 Parallel inductance and capacitance.

We can approach the analysis of this circuit either completely by phasor diagram or by calculation but preferably by a combination of both, using the phasor diagram to clarify the process and ultimately to confirm the result obtained by calculation, as follows.

First, consider the two separate series circuits L, R_L and C, R_C which are both connected to the voltage V and find their currents and phase angles relative to this common voltage.

Impedance of inductive branch (circuit L),

$$Z_L = \sqrt{R^2 + X_L^2} \ \tan^{-1} \frac{X_L}{R}$$

then

$$I_L = \frac{V}{Z_L}$$

Also impedance of capacitive branch (circuit C),

$$Z_C = \sqrt{R^2 + X_C^2} \ \tan^{-1} \frac{X_C}{R}$$

and

$$I_C = \frac{V}{Z_C}$$

[It is not worth drawing phasor diagrams at this stage as for example Fig. 3.6 (ii) because these lead to V in terms of I which is the wrong way round, we need I in terms of V, thus requiring an additional step.]

V now becomes the reference phasor for the diagram since it is common to both circuits as shown in Fig. 3.10 (ii). I_L and I_C are drawn of length according to their calculated values and the scale chosen and at the appropriate angles ϕ_L and ϕ_C to the reference phasor. On completion of the parallelogram, the diagonal gives the total current, I. This process is given more realism if illustrated by a practical example. Values have been chosen to simplify the arithmetic.

EXAMPLE:

In the circuit of Fig. 3.10 (i),

$$V = 221\ V\ , \quad f = 796\ Hz\ , \quad L = 2.4\ mH\ ,$$

$$R_L = 5\ \Omega\ , \quad C = 25\ \mu F \quad and \quad R_C = 15\ \Omega$$

Determine the main current, I.

$$\omega = 2\pi f = 2\pi \times 796 = 5,000\ rads/s$$

Circuit L:

$$X_L = \omega L = 5000 \times 2.4 \times 10^{-3} = 12\ \Omega$$

$$|Z_L| = \sqrt{5^2 + 12^2} = 13\ \Omega$$

$$\phi_L = \tan^{-1} \frac{12}{5} = \tan^{-1} 2.4 = 67.4°$$

$$\therefore \quad I_L = \frac{V}{Z_L} = \frac{221\ \angle 0°}{13\ \angle 67.4°} = 17\ \angle{-67.4°}\ A$$

(the angle is negative therefore I_L is lagging on V).

Circuit C:

$$X_C = -\frac{1}{\omega C} = -\frac{1}{5000 \times 25 \times 10^{-6}} = \frac{-10^3}{5 \times 25} = -8\ \Omega$$

$$|Z_C| = \sqrt{15^2 + (-8)^2} = 17\ \Omega$$

$$\phi_C = \tan^{-1} \frac{-8}{15} = -28.1°$$

$$\therefore \quad I_C = \frac{V}{Z_C} = \frac{221\ \angle 0°}{17\ \angle{-28.1°}} = 13\ \angle 28.1°\ A$$

(the angle is positive, therefore I_C leads V).

The phasor diagram can now be drawn showing I_L and I_C relative to the reference phasor V. This is, in fact, the diagram used for Fig. 3.10 (ii). Completion of the parallelogram gives at the diagonal from O the modulus and angle of the resultant current, I, measuring on the particular scale shown $20.3 \angle -28°$ A.

We can calculate I by first resolving I_L and I_C into their rectangular coordinates and adding the real parts together, similarly the imaginary parts (see Section 1.3.4). These form the rectangular coordinates for I, due care being necessary as to signs.

Real component of $I = I_L \cos \phi_L + I_C \cos \phi_C$

$= 17 \cos -67.4° + 13 \cos 28.1° = 6.533 + 11.468 = 18.0$

(both components lie on the real axis to the right of the imaginary axis and are therefore positive).

Imaginary component of $I = I_L \sin \phi_L + I_C \sin \phi_C$

$= 17 \sin -67.4° + 13 \sin 28.1° = -15.695 + 6.123$

$= -9.57$

(the imaginary component of I_L is negative because it lies below the real axis), i.e. $I = 18 - j9.57$.

Then

$$|I| = \sqrt{18^2 + (-9.57)^2} = \sqrt{324 + 91.58} = 20.39 \text{ A}$$

$$\phi = \tan^{-1} \frac{-9.57}{18.0} = \tan^{-1} -0.532 = -28°$$

i.e.,

$$\underline{I = 20.39 \quad \angle -28° \text{ A}}$$

128

confirmed by the measurements made on the phasor diagram. This clearly demonstrates how useful the diagram is, not only as a check on arithmetic but also in keeping angles and their signs correct, which is, without doubt, one of the pitfalls in this type of calculation.

As an oft-repeated reminder of what the angle means, since f = 796 Hz, the cycle period = 1/796 secs and an angle of 28° represents

$$\frac{28}{360} \times \frac{1000}{796} \text{ ms} = 0.098 \text{ ms}$$

i.e. the current wave follows the voltage wave 0.098 ms later.

We can also calculate fully using complex notation which begins to show its value in these more complicated circuits:

$$Z_L = R_L + j\omega L = 5 + j12$$

$$Z_C = R_C - \frac{j}{\omega C} = 15 - j8$$

$$I_L = \frac{V}{Z_L} = \frac{221}{5 + j12}$$

$$I_C = \frac{V}{Z_C} = \frac{221}{15 - j8}$$

$$I = I_L + I_C = \frac{221}{5 + j12} + \frac{221}{15 - j8} = 221\left(\frac{1}{5 + j12} + \frac{1}{15 - j8}\right)$$

Rationalizing both fractions:

$$I = 221 \left(\frac{1}{5 + j12} \times \frac{5 - j12}{5 - j12} + \frac{1}{15 - j8} \times \frac{15 + j8}{15 + j8} \right)$$

$$= 221 \left(\frac{5 - j12}{5^2 + 12^2} + \frac{15 + j8}{15^2 + 8^2} \right) = 221 \left(\frac{5 - j12}{169} + \frac{15 + j8}{289} \right)$$

$$= 1.308 (5 - j12) + 0.765 (15 + j8)$$

$$= 6.540 - j15.696 + 11.475 + j6.120$$

(add real terms together and imaginary (j) terms together)

$$I = 18.02 - j9.58$$

an answer almost identical with the first.

3.7   RESONANCE

We now come to one of the essential and perhaps even fascinating fundamental concepts on which many of our techniques are based, that of *resonance* and although this is really proper to the foregoing sections, it is of such importance that it warrants one of its own. The derivation of the word (Latin, resonare, to echo or resound) tends to place it within the audio frequency range but electrically the word is used for any frequency.

Many elastic materials (and even a stretched wire is elastic, provided that it is not over-stretched) have a natural period of vibration, a most common example is with us all, it is the human voice in which the vocal cords are tensioned by muscles so that as air passes them they vibrate and produce sound. At any instant each cord is vibrating at its *resonant frequency*, that is, the one at which it vibrates naturally.

Without resonance therefore we would be speechless, nor would we even have music for be it the string of a violin, the reed and air column of an organ pipe or clarinet, the taut skin of a drum, each has a resonant frequency, often variable by the musician, which results in vibration and sound.

In the world of electronics there is a close parallel, circuits can be made to respond more to one particular frequency than to any other, for this the word *tuned* is often used. When a violinist slackens or tightens his violin string to match the pitch of a tuning fork, he is tuning the string by changing its resonant frequency. In the same way a listener tunes a radio receiver to a particular radio station by changing the resonant frequency of the tuning circuits.

We consider the series resonant circuit first, for apart from being the simplest, through it most facets of resonance can be explained. It is most easily introduced by considering the series circuit shown in Fig. 3.9 but with the condition that $V_L = V_C$ and therefore $V_L - V_C = 0$, the circuit exhibits no reactance and is said to be resonant. The phase angle ϕ reduces to zero and the phasor V falls to the real axis, becoming coincident with V_R. For this condition to arise, since $V_L = V_C$, $IX_L = IX_C$, hence $X_L = X_C$, i.e.

$$2\pi f_0 L = \frac{1}{2\pi f_0 C} \quad \therefore 4\pi^2 f_0^2 = \frac{1}{LC} \quad \therefore f_0^2 = \frac{1}{4\pi^2 LC}$$

i.e.
$$f_0 = \frac{1}{2\pi\sqrt{LC}}$$

where f_0 is the resonant frequency.

Also if

$$\omega_0 = 2\pi f_0$$

131

then
$$2\pi f_0 = \frac{1}{\sqrt{LC}} \quad \therefore \quad \omega_0 = \frac{1}{\sqrt{LC}}$$

These are important formulae to remember, they are correct for the series circuit but parallel circuits modify them slightly, but so little that they can be used generally, the more complicated ones being employed only when great accuracy is required.

Now, since

$$Z = \sqrt{R^2 + (X_L - X_C)^2}$$

and

$$X_L = X_C \qquad Z = \sqrt{R^2} = R$$

i.e. the impedance of the circuit at resonance is equal to the value of the resistance and this is the lowest obtainable because any value for $(X_L - X_C)$ other than 0 increases Z. Hence the circuit current is maximum at f_0.

The fact that the reactances cancel does not mean that there is no reactive voltage, on the contrary, because at resonance the current is maximum, the voltages across the inductance and capacitance are both at their highest but even so, they cancel. There is, in fact, a *resonant rise* in voltage across all components due to the resonant rise in current.

As we find again and again the full picture is completely revealed by a set of graphs which we can quite easily produce ourselves. Circuit values are chosen for arithmetic ease, (shown in Fig. 3.11) but this in no way invalidates the conclusions. Also it is more convenient to work to a scale of ω rather than f as shown in Table 3.3 which gives the calculations at a few frequencies as a guide. The full curves are plotted in Fig. 3.11. This is a complete analysis of a series resonant circuit and although the calculations follow from our foregoing studies, for revision the formulae are repeated with the calculations for $\omega = 600$ rads/s.

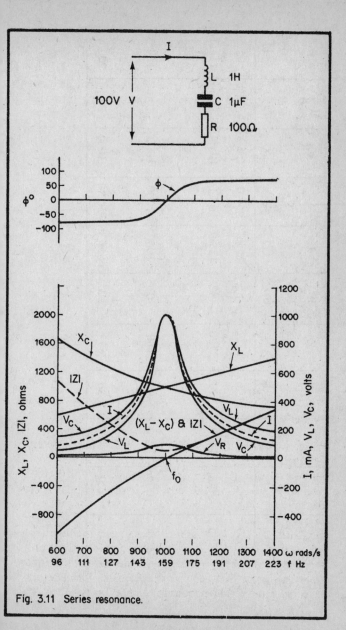

Fig. 3.11 Series resonance.

ω rads/s (1)	X_L Ω (2)	X_C Ω (3)	$(X_L - X_C)$ Ω (4)	$\lvert Z \rvert$ Ω (5)	$\phi°$ (6)	I mA (7)	V_L volts (8)	V_C volts (9)	V_R volts (10)	f Hz (11)
600	600	1667	−1067	1072	−85	93.3	56.0	155.5	9.3	95.5
700	700	1429	− 729	736	−82	135.9	95.1	194.2	13.6	111.4
......	......	......	......	......	......	......	......	......	......	......
1000	1000	1000	0	100	0	1000	1000	1000	100	159.2
......	......	......	......	......	......	......	......	......	......	......
1400	1400	714	686	693	82	144.3	202.0	103.0	14.4	222.8

TABLE 3.3   Calculations for Fig. 3.11

Col. 2 $X_L = \omega L = 600 \times 1$ $= 600\ \Omega$

Col. 3 $X_C = \dfrac{1}{\omega C} = \dfrac{10^6}{600 \times 1}$ $\approx 1667\ \Omega$

Col. 4 $= \text{Col. 2} - \text{Col. 3} = 600 - 1667 = -1067\ \Omega\ (= X)$

Col. 5 $|Z| = \sqrt{R^2 + X^2} = \sqrt{100^2 + (-1067)^2} = 1072\ \Omega$

Col. 6 $\phi = \tan^{-1} \dfrac{X}{R} = \tan^{-1} \dfrac{-1067}{100}$ $= -85°$

Col. 7 $I = \dfrac{V}{|Z|} = \dfrac{100}{1072} \times 1000$ $= 93.3\ \text{mA}$

Col. 8 $V_L = IX_L = \dfrac{93.3}{1000} \times 600$ $= 56\ \text{V}$

Col. 9 $V_C = IX_C = \dfrac{93.3}{1000} \times 1667$ $= 155.5\ \text{V}$

Col. 10 $V_R = IR = \dfrac{93.3}{1000} \times 100$ $= 9.3\ \text{V}$

Col. 11 $f = \dfrac{\omega}{2\pi} = 600/2\pi$ $= 95.5\ \text{Hz}$

Although correctly X_C should be given a negative value, so
placing its graph below the horizontal axis, the sign has been
ignored so that X_L and X_C are plotted together to show more
clearly how they become equal at $\omega = 1000$ rads/s, (i.e.
$f_0 = 159$ Hz is the resonant frequency). As the frequency is
varied from below this resonant value to above, considerable

changes occur especially within about 10% of f_0, chiefly:

(i)   the circuit current rises to its maximum value at f_0 where it is limited only by the resistance and is equal to V/R;

(ii) the modulus of the impedance falls to a minimum and at f_0 is equal to the resistance;

(iii) the angle of the impedance swings over from a large negative value to a large positive one;

(iv) the voltages across the reactances rise to a high value at f_0, in fact they become much greater than the applied voltage. This demonstrates the resonant rise in voltage where, for this particular circuit, the voltage developed across both L and C at resonance is ten times the applied voltage;

(v)   at frequencies below f_0, X_C predominates, making $(X_L - X_C)$ negative, that is, the circuit is capacitive with ϕ negative. At frequencies above f_0, X_L predominates and the circuit is inductive with ϕ positive. At more than about 10% off resonance $|Z|$ is very nearly equal to $(X_L - X_C)$ which is shown in Fig. 3.11 by the fact that the curve of $|Z|$ meets that of $(X_L - X_C)$ slightly above $\omega = 1100$. If at frequencies below f_0 $|Z|$ were plotted below the horizontal axis it would be found to be coincident with $(X_L - X_C)$ below about $\omega = 900$.

The use of the resonant circuit may be appreciated from the single example of a radio receiver input circuit. Suppose the voltage V is supplied by the receiver aerial (not 100 V in this case but of the order of μV or mV) and the subsequent stage in the receiver fed by the voltage developed across L or C. At the frequency at which they resonate there will be maximum magnification of the aerial voltage, in other words that particular frequency has been *selected* from all others. Actually we normally talk in terms of a *band* of frequencies because from Fig. 3.11 it is clear that frequencies quite close to f_0 have a voltage magnification only a little less than that of f_0 itself. This is not as detrimental as may at first seem and is considered later.

The resonant frequency of the radio receiver input circuit is usually changed by making C variable and coupling it mechanically to the tuning control.

EXAMPLE:
The aerial circuit of a radio receiver consists of an inductor of 0.215 mH in series with a variable capacitor having a range from 45 to 415 pF. What is the range of frequencies tuned and what are the corresponding wavelengths?

When capacitor is set at 45 pF,

$$f_0 = \frac{1}{2\pi\sqrt{0.215 \times 10^{-3} \times 45 \times 10^{-12}}}$$

[there are some awkward powers of 10 here. First change 0.215×10^{-3} to 215×10^{-6} to make the total exponent of 10 under the root sign an even number (10^{-18}). To bring out from under the root sign the exponent is then halved (10^{-9}), it can then be moved to the numerator by changing the exponent sign. This is shown below step by step].

$$f_0 = \frac{1}{2\pi\sqrt{215 \times 10^{-6} \times 45 \times 10^{-12}}}$$

$$= \frac{1}{2\pi\sqrt{215 \times 45 \times 10^{-18}}} = \frac{1}{2\pi \times 10^{-9} \sqrt{215 \times 45}}$$

$$= \frac{10^9}{2\pi\sqrt{9675}} = \frac{10^9}{2\pi \times 98.36} = \frac{10^9}{618} = \underline{1618 \text{ kHz}}$$

When capacitor is set at 415 pF

$$f_0 = \frac{1}{2\pi\sqrt{0.215 \times 10^{-3} \times 415 \times 10^{-12}}} = \frac{10^9}{2\pi\sqrt{215 \times 415}}$$

$$= \frac{10^9}{2\pi\sqrt{89225}} = \frac{10^9}{2\pi \times 298.7} = \underline{532.8 \text{ kHz}}$$

The tuning range is therefore $\underline{1618 - 532.8 \text{ kHz}}$.

Wavelength,

$$\lambda = \frac{c}{f} \text{ m}$$

where c = velocity of propagation of radio waves = 3×10^8 m/s (Sect. 1.2.6)

$$\therefore \qquad \lambda_1 = \frac{3 \times 10^8}{532.8 \times 10^3} = 563 \text{ m}$$

$$\lambda_2 = \frac{3 \times 10^8}{1618 \times 10^3} = 185 \text{ m}$$

$\therefore$ Equivalent wavelength range is $185 - 563$ m, so giving

Capacitor	45	415 pF
Wavelength	185	563 m
Frequency	1618	532.8 kHz.

EXAMPLE:
It is required to tune a 3 mH inductor to a radio transmission on 1500 m. What value capacitor is required?

$$f_0 = \frac{c}{\lambda} = \frac{3 \times 10^8}{1500} = 2 \times 10^5 \text{ Hz}$$

Now

$$f_0 = \frac{1}{2\pi\sqrt{LC}} \quad \therefore 2\pi f_0 = \frac{1}{\sqrt{LC}} \quad \therefore 4\pi^2 f_0^2 = \frac{1}{LC}$$

$$\therefore \quad 4\pi^2 f_0^2 L = \frac{1}{C} \quad \therefore C = \frac{1}{4\pi^2 f_0^2 L} \ F$$

i.e.
$$C = \frac{10^{12}}{4\pi^2 \times (2 \times 10^5)^2 \times 3 \times 10^{-3}} \ pF$$

$$= \frac{10^{15}}{12\pi^2 \times 4 \times 10^{10}} = \frac{10^5}{48\pi^2} = \underline{211 \ pF}.$$

3.7.1 Q-Factor in Resonant Circuits

If it is accepted that the requirement of a resonant circuit is to obtain as high a resonant rise across either reactive component as possible at one particular frequency to the exclusion of all others (it is not quite like this as will be shown in the next section) then the first component to consider is obviously resistance for this limits the circuit current I (Fig. 3.11) and hence the resonant voltage rise across L or C. As an example, if in the circuit shown, R is reduced to 50 Ω, then I is doubled, V_L and V_C are doubled and the circuit looks very much more efficient. We have already found a measure of circuit efficiency or quality in Q-factor and from Section 3.4 it is clear that in a tuned circuit nearly all the resistance lies within the inductor for which, at resonance:

$$Q_0 \text{ (the value of Q at resonance)} = \frac{2\pi f_0 L}{R}$$

and since
$$f_0 = \frac{1}{2\pi\sqrt{LC}}$$

$$Q_0 = \frac{2\pi L}{R} \times \frac{1}{2\pi\sqrt{LC}} = \frac{L}{R\sqrt{LC}}$$

There is a little juggling with root signs next so each step is shown:

Multiply numerator and denominator by $\sqrt{L}$

$$Q_0 = \frac{L\sqrt{L}}{R\sqrt{LC} \times \sqrt{L}} \quad \text{and since } \sqrt{LC} = \sqrt{L} \times \sqrt{C}$$

$$Q_0 = \frac{L\sqrt{L}}{R\sqrt{L} \times \sqrt{L} \times \sqrt{C}} = \frac{L\sqrt{L}}{R\,L\sqrt{C}} = \frac{1}{R} \cdot \frac{\sqrt{L}}{\sqrt{C}} =$$

$$= \frac{1}{R}\sqrt{\frac{L}{C}}$$

[which could also be resolved using exponents instead of root signs:

$$Q_0 = \frac{L^1}{R \cdot L^{1/2} C^{1/2}}$$

— multiply numerator and denominator by $L^{-1/2}$ (i.e. add the exponents), remembering that $L^0 = 1$,

$$Q_0 = \frac{L^{1-1/2}}{R \cdot C^{1/2}} = \frac{L^{1/2}}{R \cdot C^{1/2}} = \frac{1}{R}\left(\frac{L}{C}\right)^{1/2} \text{ or } \frac{1}{R}\sqrt{\frac{L}{C}}\,]$$

showing mathematically that Q_0 is inversely proportional to R, which confirms the reasoning above.

Reducing resistance is however, not always easy or even possible especially where the higher frequencies are concerned because R is actually higher than it would be in a dc or low-frequency circuit. Because it is now a different sort of R, it is called the *effective resistance* or quite commonly the *ac resistance.*

When an alternating current flows through a wire, even a straight one, most of the magnetic flux which emanates from the centre of the wire cuts the outer sections and then collapses through them, itself generating a counter (or back) emf in the wire by the normal process of self-induction. Not all the flux however reaches as far as the surface of the wire thus the flux change at the centre is greater than that at the surface so causing a greater centre than surface impedance. Accordingly more of the current flows at the surface (or skin) of the conductor than at the centre, giving rise to the term *Skin Effect.* Effectively therefore, the resistance of the conductor rises.

This is a somewhat incomplete explanation and the process defies simple mathematical analysis, thus we rely on measurement to establish practical calculation tables. The effect is expressed as the ratio between the ac resistance at a given frequency and that at zero frequency (dc), i.e. R_{ac}/R_{dc} and has been found to vary with both the diameter of the conductor and the square root of the frequency. Larger diameter wires have a higher comparative ac resistance than fine ones thus coils for use at radio frequencies are often wound with several strands of fine wire twisted together but insulated from each other and equivalent in total cross-sectional area to the wire they replace.

A typical example of the rise in ac resistance with frequency is given by the figures below showing how many times the resistance of a 0.2 mm diameter copper wire effectively increases at various frequencies up to 100 MHz:

Frequency (MHz)	0.1	0.5	1.0	5	10	100
R_{ac}/R_{dc}	1.00	1.03	1.10	2.00	2.60	7.87

thus at the higher frequencies (e.g. television broadcast frequencies run from about 40 MHz upwards), skin effect may seriously hamper efforts to make Q_0 high.

Further considering the formula for Q_0, we see that it is not only inversely proportional to R but also directly proportional to $\sqrt{L/C}$, so the second method of raising Q_0 is to make L/C high. For any given resonant frequency the product of L and C is fixed so any combination having the same product will give the same resonant frequency Thus we can change the L/C ratio at will provided that the product LC remains constant.

EXAMPLE:
What is the effect on Q_0 for the circuit of Fig. 3.11 if the inductance is doubled and the capacitance changed accordingly?

Resonant frequency,

$$f_0 = \frac{1}{2\pi\sqrt{LC}} = \frac{1}{2\pi\sqrt{1 \times 1 \times 10^{-6}}} = \frac{10^3}{2\pi} = 159.2 \text{ Hz}$$

$$\omega_0 = 2\pi f_0 = 2\pi \times \frac{10^3}{2\pi} = 1000 \text{ rads/s}$$

$$Q_0 = \frac{\omega_0 L}{R} = \frac{1000 \times 1}{100} = 10$$

If L is doubled, C must be halved so that $2L \times C/2$ is still equal to LC, i.e. L = 2 H, C = 0.5 μF.

[Check f_0:

$$f_0 = \frac{1}{2\pi\sqrt{2 \times 0.5 \times 10^{-6}}} = \frac{10^3}{2\pi}$$

as above, i.e. the resonant frequency has not changed] and

Q_0 for 2nd circuit equals

$$\frac{\omega_0 L}{R} = \frac{1000 \times 2}{100} = 20, \text{ i.e. } \underline{Q_0 \text{ has been doubled.}}$$

Knowing Q_0 also helps in calculation of the resonant rise in voltage across the reactive components for since

$$V_L = IX_L \text{ and at resonance } I = \frac{V}{R}$$

(where V is the applied voltage), then

$$V_L = \frac{V}{R} X_L$$

$$\therefore \quad V_L = V \cdot Q_0 \text{ since } Q_0 = \frac{X_L}{R}$$

Hence Q_0 also expresses the voltage magnification of a resonant circuit. This is illustrated in Fig. 3.12 which looks again at the circuit of Fig. 3.11 and shows the curve for V_C plotted to a different scale and excluding frequencies remote from resonance. This is the curve labelled $Q_0 = 10$. V_C doubles at resonance when $Q_0 = 20$ and increases to 5 times when $Q_0 = 50$. The circuits from which the curves are drawn are:

$$Q_0 = 10 \quad L = 1\,H \quad C = 1\,\mu F \quad R = 100\,\Omega$$

$$Q_0 = 20 \quad L = 1\,H \quad C = 1\,\mu F \quad R = 50\,\Omega$$

$$Q_0 = 50 \quad L = 5\,H \quad C = 0.2\,\mu F \quad R = 100\,\Omega$$

thus the second curve shows the increase in voltage magnification when R is reduced while the third demonstrates the effect of increased L/C ratio.

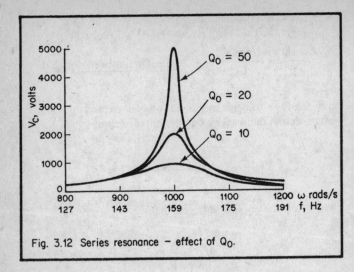

Fig. 3.12 Series resonance – effect of Q_0.

EXAMPLE:
A radio receiver tuned circuit resonates at 465 kHz. The inductance of the coil is 532 μH with Q at resonance of 70. What are the values of the effective resistance of the coil and of the capacitor? Calculate the voltage developed across the capacitor when a voltage of 2 mV at 465 kHz is applied.

$$L = 532 \times 10^{-6} \text{ H} \qquad f_0 = 465 \times 10^3 \text{ Hz}$$

$$Q_0 = 70 \qquad V = 2 \times 10^{-3} \text{ V}$$

Let effective resistance = R Ω

$$\omega_0 L = 2\pi \times 465 \times 10^3 \times 532 \times 10^{-6} = 1554 \ \Omega$$

and since

$$Q_0 = \frac{\omega_0 L}{R}, \quad R = \frac{\omega_0 L}{Q_0} = \frac{1554}{70} = \underline{22.2 \ \Omega}$$

Also

$$f_0 = \frac{1}{2\pi\sqrt{LC}}$$

144

$$\therefore \quad C = \frac{1}{4\pi^2 f_0^2 L} = \frac{10^{12}}{4\pi^2 \times 465^2 \times 10^6 \times 532 \times 10^{-6}} \quad pF$$

$$= \underline{220\ pF}.$$

Voltage developed across C at resonance

$$= VQ_0 = 2 \times 10^{-3} \times 70 = \underline{0.14\ V}.$$

3.7.2 Selectivity

One might be forgiven for now deciding that to obtain as low a value of R as possible and then make L/C very high is all that is necessary for good resonant circuit design, that is, for the circuit to accept one frequency only. There are occasions when this is true as for example in switching or relay circuits where the circuit operates when a pure tone (sine wave) at some given frequency is received. For most transmission considerations, however, another factor is of prime importance, frequency *bandwidth*, and this is perhaps best introduced by considering those frequencies recognized by the human ear, extending from about 20 Hz to 16,000 Hz. This defines the *band* of frequencies, the bandwidth is simply 16,000 − 20 = 15.98 kHz. A good *communication channel* (radio, telephone or even the air-path between people) carries all these frequencies equally well but for particular purposes or economy we often make do with less and the quality or goodness of an audio channel depends on its bandwidth as is demonstrated by the figures in Table 3.4.

Now it is a fact that audio frequencies cannot be broadcast directly by radio and even if they could we should be limited to one radio station for more would simply interfere with each other. Audio frequencies are impressed on a higher *carrier* frequency which can be transmitted, generally, from about 150 kHz upwards (although lower frequencies can be and are used). When this happens the radio transmission

Range Hz	Approx. Bandwidth	Classification
20 – 16,000	16 kHz	High Fidelity Music
50 – 10,000	10 kHz	Good Quality Music
50 – 6000	6 kHz	Medium Quality Music, High Quality Speech
300 – 3400	3 kHz	Commercial Quality Speech Telephone Channel
400 – 2400	2 kHz	Poor Quality Speech

TABLE 3.4   Bandwidths of Audio Channels

does not consist of a single frequency but of a band of frequencies usually (the word "usually" must be used because so many variations exist) centred on the central carrier frequency and of a total bandwidth equal to twice the highest audio frequency. As we see from the table, the width of the band in any particular case depends on the type and quality of the information being transmitted, and although so far we have talked in terms of bandwidths of a few kHz for audio reception, other systems which require transmission of information at a much faster rate, such as colour television, need bandwidths of several MHz.

We can leave actual figures at this point for these have only been employed to develop the main point, which is that very frequently a sharp curve such as Q = 50 on Fig. 3.12 may not be required, a flat top equal in width to the band of frequencies being carried by the particular channel may be needed. But such an ideal does not exist and it is usually sufficient to design for all frequencies within the band to be selected within a certain range of levels, thereafter the curve falling away as steeply as possible. The ideal characteristic is shown dotted in Fig. 3.13, all frequencies within the band producing the same high response (V_C, V_L or I), other frequencies outside this band having none. The typical practical curve shows:

(i)   the perfect flat top is not possible and the response over the band varies, with maximum at the centre;

(ii)   there will be some response at frequencies outside the band required, decreasing as the deviation from f_0 increases.

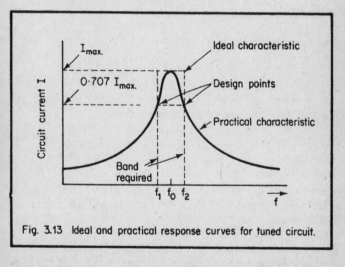

Fig. 3.13 Ideal and practical response curves for tuned circuit.

Clearly from Fig. 3.12 the higher values of Q produce the lower bandwidths so a formula involving Q seems possible. For if the bandwidth is specified as between the points where the net reactance (X) has risen (from zero at f_0) to a value equal to the circuit resistance R (shown as f_1 and f_2 on Fig. 3.13), then

147

$$Z = \sqrt{R^2 + X^2}$$

and because we have made $R = X$

$$Z = \sqrt{2R^2} = \sqrt{2} \cdot R$$

and

$$I = \frac{V}{Z} = \frac{V}{\sqrt{2}R}$$

but V/R is the current I_{max} at f_0

$\therefore$
$$I = \frac{1}{\sqrt{2}} \cdot I_{max} = 0.707\, I_{max}$$

where I is the circuit current at f_1 and f_2

Also because $R = X$, i.e. $X_L - X_C = R$

$$\frac{1}{\omega_1 C} - \omega_1 L = R$$

and

$$\omega_2 L - \frac{1}{\omega_2 C} = R$$

where ω_1 and ω_2 refer to f_1 and f_2 respectively. (Note that at $\omega_1, 1/\omega_1 C$ is greater than $\omega_1 L$, at ω_2, $1/\omega_2 C$ is less than $\omega_2 L$.)

These equations become more manageable if C is eliminated. We multiply the first equation throughout by ω_1 and the second by ω_2.

$$\frac{1}{C} - \omega_1^2 L = \omega_1 R \qquad \omega_2^2 L - \frac{1}{C} = \omega_2 R$$

The two equations can now be added together (since both sides of either equation are equal, adding one equation to the other is equivalent to adding the same value to each side of it, the equality is therefore maintained).

$$\therefore \quad \frac{1}{C} - \omega_1{}^2 L + \omega_2{}^2 L - \frac{1}{C} = \omega_1 R + \omega_2 R$$

$$\therefore \quad L(\omega_2{}^2 - \omega_1{}^2) = R(\omega_1 + \omega_2)$$

$$\therefore \quad L(\omega_2 + \omega_1)(\omega_2 - \omega_1) = R(\omega_1 + \omega_2)$$

$$[a^2 - b^2 = (a + b)(a - b)]$$

$$\therefore \quad L(\omega_2 - \omega_1) = R$$

$$\therefore \quad \omega_2 - \omega_1 = \frac{R}{L}$$

$$\therefore \quad f_2 - f_1 = \frac{R}{2\pi L}$$

(dividing both sides by 2π) and

$$\frac{f_2 - f_1}{f_0} = \frac{R}{2\pi f_0 L} = \frac{1}{Q}$$

(dividing both sides by f_0 and remembering that $Q = 2\pi f_0 L/R$)

Thus, bandwidth

$$f_2 - f_1 = \frac{f_0}{Q} \text{ Hz}$$

another important relationship simplified by use of Q.

This confirms that high Q results in low bandwidth, thus given a certain value of R, a choice of L/C ratio must be made to produce a Q giving the best compromise between selectivity and bandwidth.

EXAMPLE:

A tuned circuit has a pass-band of 9 kHz with an L/C ratio of 16,900 and Q of 52. Calculate the resonant frequency and the value of each component.

$$f_2 - f_1 \text{ (as in Fig. 3.13)} = 9 \text{ kHz} = \frac{f_0}{52}$$

$$f_0 = 52 \times 9 \text{ kHz} = \underline{468 \text{ kHz}}$$

$$Q_0 = \frac{1}{R} \sqrt{\frac{L}{C}} \quad \therefore R \cdot Q_0 = \sqrt{\frac{L}{C}} \quad \therefore R = \frac{1}{Q_0} \sqrt{\frac{L}{C}}$$

i.e.
$$R = \frac{1}{52} \sqrt{16900} = \frac{130}{52} = \underline{2.5 \ \Omega}.$$

Also $\quad Q_0 = \dfrac{\omega_0 L}{R} \quad \therefore L = \dfrac{R.Q_0}{\omega_0} = \dfrac{2.5 \times 52}{2\pi \times 468 \times 10^3} \text{ H} =$

$$\underline{44.21 \ \mu H}$$

and

$$\frac{L}{C} = 16900 \quad \therefore C = \frac{L}{16900} = \frac{44.21 \times 10^{-6}}{16900} \times 10^6$$

$$= \underline{0.002616 \ \mu F}$$

3.7.3 Parallel Resonance

The general parallel circuit has already been considered in Section 3.6, with circuit in Fig. 3.10. For resonance, the phasor I in the phasor diagram must be brought into line with the phasor V. Mathematically

$$I_L = \frac{V}{R_L + j\omega L} \qquad I_C = \frac{V}{R_C - (j/\omega C)}$$

$$I = I_L + I_C$$

from which it will be found that

$$I = V\left[\left(\frac{R_L}{R_L{}^2 + \omega^2 L^2} + \frac{R_C}{R_C{}^2 + (1/\omega^2 C^2)}\right)\right.$$

$$\left. - j\left(\frac{\omega L}{R_L{}^2 + \omega^2 L^2} - \frac{\omega C}{\omega^2 C^2 R_C{}^2 + 1}\right)\right]$$

and since for resonance the total imaginary (j) terms must equate to zero,

$$\frac{\omega_0 L}{R^2 + \omega_0{}^2 L^2} - \frac{\omega_0 C}{\omega_0{}^2 C^2 R_C{}^2 + 1} = 0$$

divide throughout by ω_0

$$\therefore \qquad \frac{L}{R_L{}^2 + \omega_0{}^2 L^2} = \frac{C}{\omega_0{}^2 C^2 R_C{}^2 + 1}$$

cross multiply

$$\omega_0{}^2 L C^2 R_C{}^2 + L = C R_L{}^2 + \omega_0{}^2 L^2 C$$

we are trying to find ω_0, so bring all ω_0 terms to one side

$$\therefore \quad L - CR_L^2 = \omega_0^2(L^2C - LC^2R_C^2)$$

$$\therefore \quad L - CR_L^2 = \omega_0^2 LC(L - CR_C^2)$$

divide both sides by $(L - CR_C^2)$

$$\therefore \quad \frac{L - CR_L^2}{L - CR_C^2} = \omega_0^2 LC$$

$$\therefore \quad \omega_0^2 = \frac{1}{LC}\left(\frac{L - CR_L^2}{L - CR_C^2}\right)$$

and

$$\omega_0 = \frac{1}{\sqrt{LC}}\sqrt{\frac{L - CR_L^2}{L - CR_C^2}}$$

A rather complicated formula which shows that the parallel circuit resonant frequency is different from that of a series circuit for which the formula is simply

$$\omega_0 = \frac{1}{\sqrt{LC}}$$

Now we usually assume that the resistance in the capacitive leg is negligible, i.e. $R_C = 0$, if so:

$$\omega_0 = \frac{1}{\sqrt{LC}}\sqrt{1 - \frac{CR_L^2}{L}}$$

or as sometimes expressed:

$$\omega_0 = \sqrt{\frac{1}{LC} - \frac{R_L^2}{L^2}}$$

152

so that the resonant frequency also depends on the resistance R_L. However, in practice it is usually found that the value of CR_L^2/L is small and the complete formula reduces to that for the series case, for example, using the values for L, C and R_L in the last example, $\sqrt{1 - (CR_L^2/L)} = 0.9998$.

Returning to the full expression for the main current I, above, since at resonance the imaginary terms equate to zero,

$$I = V \left[\frac{R_L}{R_L^2 + \omega_0^2 L^2} + \frac{R_C}{R_C^2 + \dfrac{1}{\omega_0^2 C^2}} \right]$$

and by simplifying this expression, then determining Z from V/I, we should find that

$$Z_0 = \frac{L + CR_L R_C}{C(R_L + R_C)}$$

(the mathematics are straightforward but tedious, ω_0 is first eliminated by substituting the expression for ω_0^2 developed above).

In the practical circuit where $R_C \approx 0$

$$Z_0 = \frac{L}{CR_L}$$

and as expected, Z_0 has no j term, hence no angle, i.e. the impedance is purely resistive.

Other interesting features of the parallel circuit at resonance are:

(i) there is a high circulating current within the Circuit L/Circuit C loop (Fig. 3.10 (i)), the current I flowing to make up the losses in the resistance. The circulating current is $Q_0 \times I$. Again $Q_0 = (\omega_0 L)/R$;

(ii) the impedance of the circuit is maximum (for the series circuit it is minimum);

(iii) selectivity can also be determined in a similar way to that for the series circuit but in this case the bandwidth is considered at the points where the impedance falls to 0.707 of its maximum value.

3.8 TRANSFORMERS

When work is done, such as moving the cone of a loudspeaker or forcing electrons past the resistance of a lamp filament, power is required, electronic equipment must therefore have a supply. Sometimes this is provided by a battery but more often less expensively from the mains supply via a *power transformer*, the main purpose of which is to enable the equipment to draw its power from the mains but at a different voltage. It also provides safety from electric shock by isolating the equipment from the mains, for the connexion between the two is not direct but via a magnetic flux. This type of transformer has a ferromagnetic core (ferro, from Latin ferrum = iron) and is fairly well known.

A second type may not even be recognizable as a transformer for it may simply consist of two fine-wire coils adjacent on a tube (Fig. 3.16). This transformer, sometimes with one or both windings tuned by a capacitor, is mainly used in radio work for coupling circuits together at high frequency but low voltage.

We recall first one or two points already encountered:

(i) When two coils are coupled magnetically, a changing current in one winding produces an emf in the other and it is important to reaffirm that no emf is produced by a steady current, only by an increasing or decreasing one. Transformers are therefore ac devices, they cannot function on dc.

154

(ii)   Two coils have a mutual inductance of one henry if an emf of one volt is induced in one coil when the current changes uniformly at the rate of one ampere per second in the other, thus e (in Coil 2) = M x rate of change of current in Coil 1.

(iii) The coupling factor k is a convenient way of stating the degree of coupling between the coils, i.e. tight or loose. It is low (a small fraction of 1) for radio-type transformers, conversely it approaches 1 for power-type transformers.

(iv) $M = k\sqrt{L_1 L_2}$ where M is the mutual inductance and L_1 and L_2 are the separate coil inductances.

3.8.1 Phase Relationships

Now for any type of transformer (that is, whatever the value of k) and assuming no losses, we can ourselves produce a set of graphs showing the current and voltage relationships. This is probably more instructive than merely juggling with mathematical formulae for it helps us to develop a deeper understanding of each stage in the process.

Consider the circuit shown in Fig. 3.14 of a transformer with a voltage V applied to Coil 1 and with Coil 2 left *open circuit* (nothing connected to its terminals). We choose values to minimize calculation and simplify the graph scales as follows:

Transformer: Coil windings, N_1 = 800 turns, N_2 = 600 turns

Reluctance of magnetic circuit, S = 10^6 At/Wb

(At/Wb = ampere-turns per weber)

Frequency of applied voltage = 250 Hz

Assume the maximum current in Coil 1 = I_{max} = 100 mA, from this we can produce the graphs of i, the instantaneous current, Φ, the magnetic flux, V and e_1 and e_2, the induced voltages.

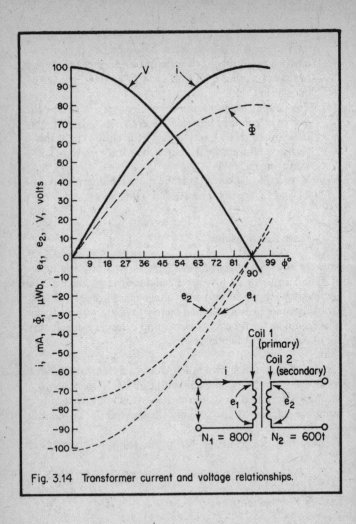

Fig. 3.14 Transformer current and voltage relationships.

First let us recall "Ohm's Law" of the magnetic circuit:

$$\text{Total flux } (\Phi) = \frac{\text{Magnetomotive force (F)}}{\text{Reluctance (S)}}$$

156

i.e.

$$\Phi(Wb) = \frac{F(At)}{S(At/Wb)}$$

where F = number of turns x current (NI).

The reluctance S is calculated from

$$\frac{10^7 \ell}{4\pi\mu_r a} \quad At/Wb$$

where ℓ and a are length and area of cross-section of the magnetic circuit, and μ_r the relative permeability.

The emf e induced in a coil is equal to the rate of change of flux multiplied by the number of turns with which it links, i.e.

$$-N \frac{d\Phi}{dt}$$

Using these formulae we can set up a table for calculation of the required graph points. Again only the first quarter-cycle is necessary to determine the relative phases.

Since

$$f = 250 \, Hz, \quad T = \frac{1}{250} \, s = 4 \, ms,$$

i.e. one quarter-cycle takes 1 ms. This might conveniently be divided into, say, 10 periods of 0.1 ms ($9°$), a compromise between the laborious amount of work arising from calculating rates of change over very small periods and the lesser accuracy of longer periods.

A suggested lay-out is given in Table 3.5 and calculations for period 3 follow as an example. Note that in the table $\delta\Phi/\delta t$ is used for the rate of change of flux because $d\Phi/dt$ refers only to an extremely small period of time,[A4.3] these periods are not in that category:

Col. 4: I_{max} is stated to be 100 mA, hence the instantaneous current at the end of the period, $i = I_{max} \sin \phi$. For period 3, $\sin \phi = \sin 27° = 0.4540$, hence $100 \sin 27° = 45.40$ mA.

Col. 5: The magnetomotive force F is $N_1 \times i = 800 \times$ Col. 4. For period 3, $F = 800 \times 45.40 \times 10^{-3}$ ampere-turns $= 36.32$ At.

Col. 6: The total flux, Φ in the core is F/S, i.e. Col. 5/S. S is given as 10^6 At/Wb, hence for period 3, $\Phi = 36.32/10^6$ Wb $= 36.32 \mu$Wb.

Col. 7: The change in flux over a period is the difference between the values in Col. 6 for that period and the previous one, i.e. for period 3, $36.32 - 24.72 = 11.60 \mu$Wb.

Col. 8: The rate of change of flux with time ($\delta\Phi/\delta t$) is given from Col. 7/Time for 1 period, i.e. Col. $7/10^{-4}$ s. For period 3, $(11.6 \times 10^{-6})/10^{-4} = 0.116$ Wb per second.

Col. 9: The voltage e_1 (counter or back-emf) produced by the changing flux is proportional to the rate of change of flux, given in Col. 8 and $e_1 = -N_1(\delta\Phi/\delta t)$. For period 3, $-800 \times 0.116 = -92.8$ V.

Col. 10: Similarly the changing flux cuts winding 2 and e_2 for period 3 $= -N_2(\delta\Phi/\delta t) = -600 \times 0.116 = 69.6$ V. A minus sign has been used but in practice this depends on the winding direction of the secondary turns relative to those of the primary.

[Note that alternatively we could have calculated $\delta i/\delta t$ and obtained e_1 from $-L_1(\delta i/\delta t)$.]

The graphs are shown for the first quarter-cycle of the current in Fig. 3.14. It is immediately evident from the figure that i and Φ are in phase, for each electron in the current is inseparable from its own magnetic field. The current wave also lags on that of the applied voltage by 90°, this is also to be expected because the primary simply acts as an inductance with the secondary having no effect, being on open circuit.

TABLE 3.5 Transformer current and voltage relationships

Period No. (1)	Time elapsed at end of period (2) ms	Equiv. degrees ϕ (3)	Current at end of period $i = I_{max} \sin\phi$ (4) mA	mmf, F at end of period $= N_1 \times i$ (5) At	Flux Φ at end of period $= F/S$ (6) μWb	Change in flux over period (7) μWb	Rate of change of flux over period $\delta\Phi/\delta t$ (8) Wb/s	$e_1 = -N_1 \frac{\delta\Phi}{\delta t}$ (9)	$e_2 = -N_2 \frac{\delta\Phi}{\delta t}$ (10)
1	0.1	9	15.64	12.51	12.51	12.51	0.1251	−100.1	−75.1
2	0.2	18	30.90	24.72	24.72	12.21	0.1221	− 97.7	−73.3
3	0.3	27	45.40	36.32	36.32	11.60	0.1160	− 92.8	−69.6
......	......	......	......	......	......	......	......	......	......
9	0.9	81	98.77	79.02	79.02	2.93	0.0293	− 23.4	− 17.6
10	1.0	90	100.0	80.00	80.00	0.98	0.0098	− 7.8	− 5.9
11	1.1	99	98.77	79.02	79.02	−0.98	−0.0098	+ 7.8	+ 5.9

Under this condition the current i is known as the *magnetizing current*.

From Lenz's Law e_1 must be equal to V and this occurs in Fig. 3.14 where the phases are also opposite. e_2 is less than e_1 because Coil 2 has a lower number of turns.

3.8.2 The Transformer Equations

The definition of the Weber as the unit of magnetic flux leads to the following formula:

$$\text{emf} = \frac{\text{Total flux cut (Wb)}}{\text{time (secs)}}$$

This refers to one turn of a coil and the emf induced is the average over the period of time, hence:

$$e_{av} = \frac{\Phi_{max}}{t}$$

and because all turns in a coil are linked by the same flux, for N turns the total average emf (E_{av}) is N times as great, i.e.

$$E_{av} = \frac{N \cdot \Phi_{max}}{t}$$

Now a flux change of Φ_{max} occurs in one-quarter of a cycle, that is, in a time 1/4f secs:

$$\therefore \quad E_{av} = \frac{N \Phi_{max}}{1/4f} = N \Phi_{max} \cdot 4f \ .$$

Because we usually work in rms values it is advantageous to convert the formula:

$$E_{max} = \frac{\pi}{2} E_{av} \quad \text{also } E_{max} = \sqrt{2} \, E_{rms}$$

$$\sqrt{2} \, E_{rms} = \frac{\pi}{2} E_{av}$$

$$\therefore \qquad E_{rms} = \frac{\pi}{2\sqrt{2}} \, E_{av} = 1.11 \, E_{av}$$

E_{rms} is normally designated by E, hence the general transformer equation is

$$E = 1.11 \times 4 \times N \times \Phi_{max} \times f$$

i.e.

$$\underline{E = 4.44 \, N \cdot \Phi_{max} \cdot f}$$

We can check this for the particular transformer used for Fig. 3.14. From Table 3.5, $\Phi_{max} = 80 \, \mu Wb$, for Coil 1 N = 800 and f = 250 Hz.

$$\therefore \quad E \text{ for Coil 1} = 4.44 \times 800 \times 80 \times 10^{-6} \times 250 = 71.04$$

and

$$E_{max} \text{ for Coil 1} = \sqrt{2} \, E = 1.414 \times 71.04 = 100.47 \, V \, .$$

E_{max} is equivalent to e_1 or V in Fig. 3.14 and it is evident that this figure and the general equation are in agreement.

3.8.3 The Transformer on Load

Since

$$E_1 = 4.44 \, N_1 \, \Phi_{max} \cdot f$$

and Φ is common to both windings, therefore

$$E_2 = 4.44 \, N_2 \, \Phi_{max} \cdot f$$

(lettering as in Fig. 3.15) so for any given transformer

$$\frac{E_1}{E_2} = \frac{N_1}{N_2}$$

i.e. the *voltage ratio* of a transformer is equal to its *turns ratio*.

If $N_2 > N_1$ the transformer is known as a *step-up* one, conversely, when $N_2 < N_1$ it is known as a *step-down* type.

EXAMPLE:
There are 1000 turns on the primary winding of an ac mains (power) transformer designed to feed 12 V from a 120 V supply. How many turns are on the secondary?

$$N_1 = 1000 \text{ t} \quad N_2 = ? \quad V_1 = 120 \text{ V} \quad V_2 = 12 \text{ V}$$

Then
$$\frac{V_1}{V_2} = \frac{N_1}{N_2} \quad \therefore \quad \frac{120}{12} = \frac{1000}{N_2}$$

$$\therefore \quad N_2 = \frac{12 \times 1000}{120} = 100 .$$

When the transformer is *on load*, that is, a circuit is connected to the secondary terminals (and here we only consider a resistive load), E_2 causes a current I_2 to flow through the secondary winding and external circuit. I_2 itself produces a magnetomotive force $N_2 I_2$ operating against the main flux created by the primary current. Hence additional primary current must flow to restore the main flux because the counter emf must always be equal to the voltage applied to the primary. Thus arises the condition that the magneto-motive force of the primary (additional to the small magnetizing current) is equal to the mmf of the secondary, therefore:

$$N_1 I_1 = N_2 I_2 \quad \therefore \quad \frac{I_1}{I_2} = \frac{N_2}{N_1} ,$$

thus the *current ratio* is the inverse of the voltage ratio and a step-up transformer in fact steps down the current.

Furthermore because when the secondary is on load a current I_1 flows in the primary to maintain flux equilibrium, then the impedance looking into the primary is calculated from V_1/I_1 where V_1 is the voltage applied.

Now

$$\frac{V_1}{V_2} = \frac{N_1}{N_2},$$

hence

$$V_1 = V_2 \cdot \frac{N_1}{N_2}$$

and

$$\frac{I_1}{I_2} = \frac{N_2}{N_1},$$

hence

$$I_1 = I_2 \cdot \frac{N_2}{N_1}$$

$$\therefore \quad Z_{IN} = \frac{V_1}{I_1} = V_2 \cdot \frac{N_1}{N_2} \times \frac{1}{I_2} \cdot \frac{N_1}{N_2} = \left(\frac{N_1}{N_2}\right)^2 \cdot \frac{V_2}{I_2}$$

and provided that the impedance of the secondary winding is small compared with that of the load

$$Z_{IN} = \left(\frac{N_1}{N_2}\right)^2 \cdot Z_L$$

Transformers are frequently designed specifically for this facility, that is, the ability to effectively change or transform an impedance. It can be shown that a generator delivers maximum power into a load when the modulus of the load impedance is equal to that of the generator (the phase angles also have a minor effect) so a transformer can be used to transform the load impedance into a different value as required by the generator. Such a transformer is known as a *matching* transformer.

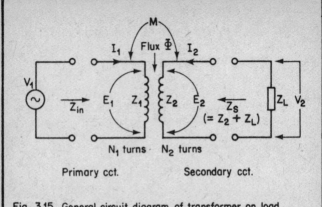

Fig. 3.15 General circuit diagram of transformer on load.

EXAMPLE:
A telephone line has an impedance of 1200 Ω non-reactive.
It is to be matched to the 600 Ω input of an amplifier. What
is the turns-ratio of a suitable matching transformer?

Using Fig. 3.15,

$$Z_L = 1200 \,\Omega \quad Z_{IN} = 600 \,\Omega \,,$$

i.e. looking into the transformer we see 600 Ω, not 1200 Ω.

$$Z_{IN} = \left(\frac{N_1}{N_2}\right)^2 Z_L \quad \therefore \frac{Z_L}{Z_{IN}} = \left(\frac{N_2}{N_1}\right)^2$$

$$\therefore \quad \sqrt{\frac{Z_L}{Z_{IN}}} = \frac{N_2}{N_1} = \sqrt{\frac{1200}{600}} = \sqrt{2} = 1.414 \,.$$

This is the turns ratio, that is $N_2 = N_1 \times 1.414$. Note that
the winding with the greater number of turns faces the higher
impedance.

3.8.4 Transformer Losses

The above considerations have usually assumed a loss-free transformer. In practice there are several losses which in design are taken into account, especially in magnetic core-type transformers:

(i)   the windings have resistance resulting in unwanted power losses which also cause a rise in temperature. The term used is *copper loss*;

(ii) all the flux set up by the current in one winding does not link with the other winding, this results in *leakage reactance:*

(iii) a ferromagnetic core causes some expenditure of energy to occur when the magnetic flux changes, this is known as *hysteresis loss* (Greek, "coming after" — the flux lags slightly on the magnetizing force);

(iv) a second core loss is due to *eddy currents*. These are tiny circulating currents set up within the core (which is also an electrical conductor) by the changing flux. These currents cause a power loss which, like all other losses, must be made good by the primary current. Eddy currents are reduced by *laminating* the core, that is, building it up from thin sheets of the ferromagnetic material, insulated from each other, or by using a *dust* core comprising the material in powdered form bound into a solid by an insulating resin;

(v) the windings have *self-capacitance* simply because the turns of copper wire lie adjacent with their insulating cover (usually a thin coating of an enamel) acting as a dielectric. At higher frequencies this causes a loss due to the shunting effect of the lower reactance of the capacitance and various methods exist for its reduction such as *wave-winding* (see Fig. 3.16) where the turns are wound in a wave fashion so that adjacent layers do not have wires running parallel.

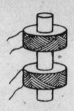

Fig. 3.16 Wave-wound air-cored transformer.

3.8.5 Radio-frequency Transformers

Much of the foregoing has included discussion of a magnetic core in the transformer, radio-frequency (rf) transformers do not employ the same type of core as power transformers for several reasons, a main one being that some of the core losses become intolerable at high frequencies. Many rf transformers are therefore air-cored but when cores are used they are usually of the dust or other special type and frequently the magnetic circuit is not closed, resulting in high reluctance.

One assumption used in deriving the general transformer equation was that all turns on both windings are embraced by the same flux. This is far from the case with an rf transformer, which, rather than having one core wound over the other as in the case of the power transformer, often and especially when tuned, has its two coils separated and possibly at some distance apart as shown in Fig. 3.16. The coefficient of coupling (k) is therefore very small and the formulae for voltage and current ratios no longer apply. A different approach is therefore appropriate.

[Readers who, at this stage, feel that they are saturated with impedance calculations might prefer to skip some of the following mathematics and calculations on the first reading. However, they lead to conclusions which should at least be

166

appreciated and possibly remembered for they show that although power and matching transformers on one hand and rf transformers on the other work on the same basic principle of magnetic coupling, the high k in the first case and low in the second produce very different components and methods of analysis.]

From the definition of mutual inductance, M (Sect. 3.8), the average value of the secondary induced voltage (see circuit, Fig. 3.15) is:

$$E_{2\,(av)} = \frac{MI_{1\,(max)}}{1/4f}$$

since I_1 rises from 0 to maximum in one quarter of a cycle.

$$= 4\,MI_{1\,(max)} \cdot f$$

and, as shown in Sect. 3.8.2

$$E_{2\,(av)} = \frac{2}{\pi} E_{2\,(max)}$$

$$\therefore \quad \frac{2}{\pi} E_{2\,(max)} = 4MI_{1\,(max)} \cdot f$$

$$\therefore \quad E_{2\,(max)} = 2\pi f MI_{1\,(max)}$$

and equally, $\qquad E_2 = 2\pi f MI_1$

or $\qquad E_2 = \omega MI_1$ and $E_1 = \omega MI_2$

which shows that a current I flowing in either winding produces an emf in the other winding equal to ωMI. Fig. 3.14 shows that a 90° phase difference exists between them so we can write for the total voltage in Coil 1:

$$V_1 = I_1 Z_1 + j\omega M I_2$$

and the secondary induced voltage is given by $-j\omega M I_1$

$$I_2 = \frac{-j\omega M I_1}{Z_2 + Z_L}$$

(we write Z_s for $Z_2 + Z_L$). Substituting for I_2 in the equation for V_1:

$$V_1 = I_1 Z_1 + j\omega M \left(\frac{-j\omega M I_1}{Z_s} \right)$$

$$\therefore \quad V_1 = I_1 Z_1 + \frac{\omega^2 M^2 I_1}{Z_s} = I_1 \left[Z_1 + \frac{(\omega M)^2}{Z_s} \right]$$

making the effective primary impedance, Z_{IN} equal to

$$Z_1 + \frac{(\omega M)^2}{Z_s}$$

that is, as though an additional impedance has been reflected from the secondary equal to $(\omega M)^2 / Z_s$. There is now enough information for a complete analysis:

(i)   calculate the total secondary impedance, $Z_s = Z_2 + Z_L$;
(ii) this impedance is reflected into the primary as $(\omega M)^2 / Z_s$
(iii) therefore the effective primary impedance $Z_{IN} = Z_1 + (\omega M)^2 / Z_s$;
(iv) calculate the primary current if V_1 is known or V_1 if I_1 is known;
(v)   calculate the secondary induced emf, $E_2 = -j\omega M I_1$;
(vi) calculate the secondary current I_2 from $(-j\omega M I_1)/Z_s$.

The following example demonstrates this and also gives practice in complex notation.

EXAMPLE:
An air-cored rf transformer has two similar coils of inductance 1.5 mH with a coupling factor k = 0.2. A 100 Ω resistor is connected to the secondary coil. If the coil resistances can be considered negligible compared with their reactances what are the primary and secondary currents if 1 V is applied to the primary at 159.2 kHz?

Using symbols as in Fig. 3.15:

$$L_1 = L_2 = 1.5 \times 10^{-3} \text{ H} \quad k = 0.2 \quad Z_L = 100 \,\Omega$$

$$V_1 = 1 \text{ V} \quad f = 159.2 \text{ kHz}$$

$$\omega = 2\pi \times 159.2 \times 10^3 = 10^6 \text{ rads/s}$$

$$\omega L_1 = \omega L_2 = 10^6 \times 1.5 \times 10^{-3} = 1500 \,\Omega$$

$$M = k\sqrt{L_1 L_2} = 0.2\sqrt{1.5 \times 1.5} = 0.3 \text{ mH} = 0.3 \times 10^{-3} \text{ H}$$

$$\omega M = 10^6 \times 0.3 \times 10^{-3} = 300$$

$$(\omega M)^2 = 9 \times 10^4$$

$$Z_2 = j\omega L_2 = j1500 \,\Omega$$

$$Z_L = 100 \,\Omega \quad \therefore \quad Z_s = Z_2 + Z_L = 100 + j1500$$

Then

$$\frac{(\omega M)^2}{Z_s} = \frac{9 \times 10^4}{100 + j1500} = \frac{900}{1 + j15} = \frac{900(1 - j15)}{1^2 + 15^2}$$

$$= \frac{900(1 - j15)}{226} = 3.98 - j59.7$$

(rationalization, see Section 1.3.4).

Primary impedance

$$Z_1 = 0 + j1500$$

Adding in the reflected impedance gives

$$Z_{IN} = 0 + j1500 + 3.98 - j59.7 = 3.98 + j1440$$

Let us pause to see what has happened so far. If the secondary had been on open circuit, Z_L would have been infinitely large and $(\omega M)^2/Z_s$ zero with no impedance reflected into the primary. The primary impedance would therefore have been simply that of Coil 1, which accordingly would absorb practically no power from the supply. Now with the secondary connected to a 100 ohm resistor we find that this causes an impedance of about $4 - j60$ to be coupled back. The 4 adds a slight resistive component to the existing primary impedance (Z_{IN}) while the $-j60$ cancels out some of the primary reactance thus causing a fall in Z_{in}, consequently an increase in I_1. The resistive component of Z_{IN} causes power to be absorbed from the supply which is ultimately dissipated in the secondary load. Continuing:

$$\text{Primary Current, } I_1 = \frac{V}{Z_{IN}} = \frac{1}{3.98 + j1440}$$

$$= \frac{3.98 - j1440}{3.98^2 + 1440^2} \approx \frac{3.98 - j1440}{2073600} \approx$$

$$\approx 1.92 - j694 \ \mu A \quad (694 \ \angle -89.8°)$$

The increase in I_1 mentioned above is seen to be quite small (I_1 with secondary on open-circuit $= 666.7 \ \mu A \ \angle -90°$). This is because the coupling factor is low, although in this example an artificially high value has been used to make the change in I_1 more obvious, (practical values for k may be less than 0.01). This perhaps is an obvious feature, that is, the lower the value of k the less effect the secondary has on the primary.

170

Voltage induced in secondary,

$$E_2 = -j\omega MI_1 = \frac{-j300\,(1.92 - j694)}{10^6}\ V$$

$$= \frac{-2082 - j5.76}{10^4} = -0.2082 - j0.000576 \quad (-0.2082\,\angle 0.2°)$$

and Secondary Current, $I_2 = \dfrac{E_2}{Z_s}$

(experience will be our guide as to whether we should work with polar or complex notation — polar is slightly easier for the following):

$$Z_s = 100 + j1500 = \sqrt{100^2 + 1500^2}\,\tan^{-1}\frac{1500}{100}$$

$$= 10^2\sqrt{226}\,\tan^{-1} 15 = 1503\,\angle 86.2°$$

$$\therefore\ I_2 = \frac{-0.2082\,\angle 0.2°}{1503\,\angle 86.2°} \times 10^6\ \mu A = -138\,\underline{/0.2 - 86.2°}$$

$$= -138\,\angle -86°$$

This is in the 2nd quadrant (Section 1.3.4) making an angle of $-86°$ with the real axis, that is, $86°$ in a clockwise direction or $180 - 86 = 94°$ from the reference axis, giving $I_2 = 138\,\angle 94°$. This is shown in the phasor diagram of Fig. 3.17, which has V_1 as a reference. The diagram also illustrates some points already discussed:

(i) with the secondary winding on open-circuit, I_1 lags on V_1 by $90°$ (compare with Fig. 3.14);

(ii) when the secondary is loaded, the phasor I_1 moves towards V_1 and develops a small resistive component;

(iii) E_2 lags on I_1 by $90°$ $(-j)$ and although the transformer has a 1:1 turns ratio whereupon one might expect E_2 to

171

be equal to V_1 (as in a power transformer) it is very much less because of the low value of M.

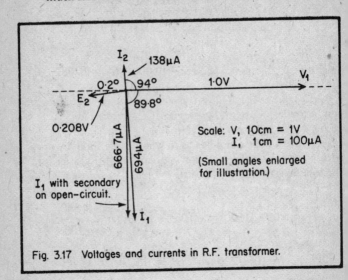

Fig. 3.17 Voltages and currents in R.F. transformer.

Scale: V, 10cm = 1V
       I, 1cm = 100μA

(Small angles enlarged for illustration.)

I_1 with secondary on open-circuit.

APPENDIX 1

ABBREVIATIONS
(mainly additional to those quoted in Book 1)

ac	alternating current
ac voltage	alternating voltage (the c is really superfluous but its use in this way is accepted generally)
approx.	approximately
cct.	circuit
col.	column
log.	logarithm
max.	maximum
min.	minimum
%	percent or percentage of
rad.	radian
rms	root mean square
sect.	section
shm	simple harmonic motion
>	is greater than
<	is less than
∞	infinity

APPENDIX 2

GRAPHS

Drawn on *squared* paper, a graph is a picture of a relationship between two variable quantities. Because it is visual rather than a single mathematical statement, many features of the relationship which are significant are more easily seen. The common type of squared, or graph paper, is known as *linear*, meaning that the squares printed horizontally are the same as those vertically. An example of a simple form of graph is as follows:

The relationship of resistance with length of 0.056 mm diameter copper wire is:

Length (ℓ)	Resistance (R)
m	Ω
1	7
2	14
5	35
10	70

We of course know from our studies that $R \propto \ell$ and therefore only one set of figures is needed for calculation of the resistance of any length. Nevertheless this is an easy example through which the simple rules for drawing a graph can be determined (see Fig. A2.1).

(i)   Two axes are drawn at right angles, the horizontal one is called the X-axis (marked OX), the vertical, the Y-axis (marked OY).

(ii)   The scales to be used are determined by the highest and lowest values to be plotted. They should be as large as possible yet conveniently suited to the squared paper in use and titled.

(iii)   Negative values on the X-axis are marked to the left of the Y-axis and similarly, negative values on the Y-axis are marked below the X-axis. This will be seen in Fig. A2.2 which follows.

(iv)   The points representing the graph values should be marked lightly and then joined. If it is desired to show the points from which the curve is derived, they may be indicated by a circled dot, ⊙ or cross, x.

Fig. A2.1 shows the graph. On a small printed page such as used here, the smaller squares are usually omitted for clarity, a small section of them is shown.

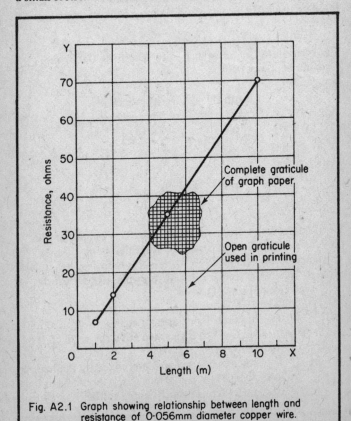

Fig. A2.1   Graph showing relationship between length and resistance of 0·056mm diameter copper wire.

The graph is a straight line, showing that the relationship is *linear*. In fact, only two points were needed to establish the graph, one of which could have been at point O because at length 0, the resistance is also 0.

Any other graph is plotted in the same way and the alternative to a linear relationship is a *non-linear* one for which points must be plotted carefully to establish the correct shape of the curve.

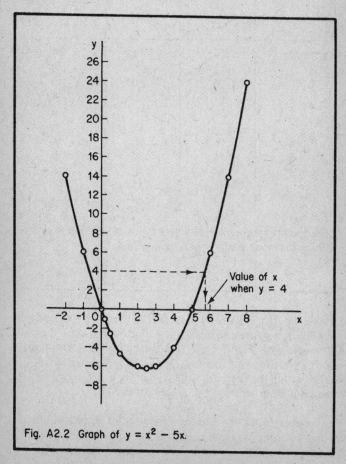

Fig. A2.2 Graph of $y = x^2 - 5x$.

Slope : Fig. A2.1 shows a rising graph (sloping upwards to the right). This is said to have a positive slope. A graph which falls downwards to the right has a negative slope. One demonstrating both types of slope and also non-linearity is shown in Fig. A2.2. This is the graph of $y = x^2 - 5x$ plotted for values of x from -2 to $+8$, the calculations being tabulated as follows:

x	x^2 (1)	$5x$ (2)	$x^2 - 5x$ Col.(1)–Col.(2)
-2	4	-10	14
-1	1	-5	6
0	0	0	0
1	1	5	-4
2	4	10	-6
3	9	15	-6
4	16	20	-4
5	25	25	0
6	36	30	6
7	49	35	14
8	64	40	24

other points are then added where there is difficulty in determining the exact position of the curve, e.g.

2.5	6.25	12.5	-6.25

From the figure it will be seen that between $x = 0$ and $x = 5$, y is negative and is therefore plotted below the X-axis. Between $x = -2$ and $x = 2.5$ the graph has a negative slope with a positive one thereafter. Values of x for given values of y within the ranges may be read off and vice versa, e.g. the value of x when $y = 4$ is read off as 5.7.

Experience in the use and interpretation of graphs will be obtained from the main text in which the variables on the Y-axis are usually current or voltage against time or angle on the X-axis.

APPENDIX 3

TRIGONOMETRY

A very old branch of mathematics, dating right back to the second century and meaning the measurement of triangles.

Section 1.1.1 in the main text introduces the fact that the value of a wave at any instant depends on the angle through which a "rotating radius" has turned. The angle itself therefore is an important constituent of wave formation and analysis, hence the usefulness of trigonometry on which we rely for ease of converting from angles to projections.

A3.1 THE RIGHT-ANGLED TRIANGLE

Triangles have three angles, hence are three-sided figures, all sides being straight lines. The sum of the angles is always $180°$, whatever the shape of the triangle. We are concerned with the right-angled triangle in which one of the angles is a right angle (rt. $\angle$), i.e. of $90°$. The sum of the two remaining angles must therefore also be $90°$.

Although it is necessary to consider a complete revolution of $360°$ as shown in Fig. A3.1, this is conveniently divided up into four quadrants and we will limit our considerations to the first quadrant before moving on to the others.

In the first quadrant the radius OR (marked h) is considered to have rotated in an anticlockwise direction from OX by an angle $\theta°$. By drawing a line perpendicular to OX from R to point P, at rt. $\angle$d triangle is produced. In such a triangle the *hypotenuse* (OR), so called from the Greek because it is opposite the rt. $\angle$, is always longer than either of the other two sides. Now considering the angle θ ($\angle\theta$), it lies between the hypotenuse and one other side (OP), this latter side we call the *adjacent* side (for $\angle\theta$). The opposite angle, marked a, also lies between the hypotenuse and one other side (PR), again called the adjacent side (for ∠a). Both angles θ and a also have *opposite* sides, for θ it is PR and for a, OP.

In summary, there are three angles in the triangle, the rt. ∠ we are not concerned with, but it must be there; for each of the other two angles we can identify an adjacent (adj.) side and an opposite (opp.) side, the side which is adjacent for one angle is opposite for the other and vice versa.

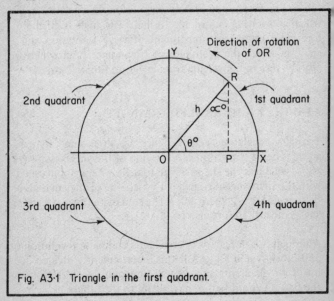

Fig. A3·1 Triangle in the first quadrant.

A3.2 TRIGONOMETRIC FUNCTIONS

From Fig. A3.1 it is clear that as either angle changes, the triangle changes in shape and both adjacent and opposite sides change in length. This in fact leads to what *sine* and *cosine* tables do, they tell us the ratios between these sides and the hypotenuse for any angle up to 90°.

The term "sine" is an adaptation of the Latin "sinus", a bend (early trigonometry included circular arcs). Cosine means the sine of the opposite angle. Thus

$$\sin \theta = \frac{\text{opposite side}}{\text{hypotenuse}} = \frac{PR}{OR}$$

$$\sin a = \frac{OP}{OR}$$

$$\cos \theta = \frac{\text{adjacent side}}{\text{hypotenuse}} = \frac{OP}{OR}$$

$$\cos a = \frac{PR}{OR}$$

so that $\sin \theta = \cos a$ and since $a = (90° - \theta)$

$$\sin \theta = \cos (90° - \theta)$$

also $\cos \theta = \sin a = \sin (90° - \theta)$.

Books of tables usually give values of sines and cosines down to 1 minute (1/60th of 1 degree). In case tables are not available, Table A3.1 at the end of this Appendix can be used, it gives values at 1° intervals. For example, the sine of 12° (written sin 12°) is 0.2079 meaning that for Fig. A3.1 if θ measures 12° the ratio PR/OR is equal to 0.2079 whatever the size of the circle.

These (sin and cos) are the basic functions and the ratios to which they refer should be memorized if possible. Both functions relate to the hypotenuse, the memory sometimes failing on which relates to the opposite side, and which to the adjacent. The name of the Russian horseman, a COSSACK may be useful for if we drop the first, middle and last letters we are left with OS AC for "opposite, sine; adjacent, cosine".

181

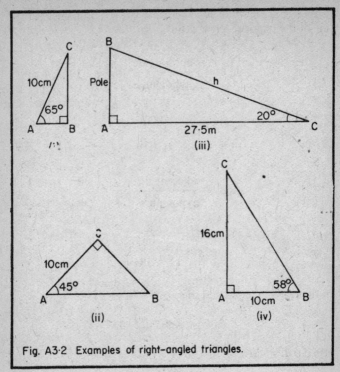

Fig. A3·2 Examples of right-angled triangles.

EXAMPLE:
In the rt. ∠d triangle ABC of Fig. A3.2 (i), AC = 10 cm and ∠BAC is 65°. What is the length of BC?

The side AC is opposite the rt. ∠ and is therefore the hypotenuse. For ∠BAC, BC is the opposite side, the length of which is required, therefore we use the sine formula:

$$\sin \angle BAC = \frac{BC}{AC} \quad \text{i.e.} \quad \sin 65° = \frac{BC}{10 \text{ cm}}$$

$$BC = 10 \sin 65° = 10 \times 0.9063 = \underline{9.063 \text{ cm.}}$$

EXAMPLE:

In the triangle ABC of Fig. A3.2 (ii), ∠ACB is a rt. ∠ and ∠BAC is 45°. The side AC is 10 cm. Calculate the side AB and ∠ABC.

AB is the hypotenuse. For ∠BAC, **AC** is the adjacent side, the length of which is known, therefore we use the cosine formula:

$$\cos \angle BAC = \frac{AC}{AB} \quad \therefore \cos 45° = \frac{10}{AB}$$

$$\therefore \qquad AB \cos 45° = 10$$

$$\therefore \qquad AB = \frac{10}{\cos 45°} = \frac{10}{0.7071} = \underline{14.14 \text{ cm.}}$$

Since all three angles add up to 180°

$$\angle ABC = 180° - (90° + 45°) = \underline{45°.}$$

A third trigonometrical form is given in Table A3.1, this is the *tangent* (tan) and for any rt. ∠d triangle as in Fig. A3.1

$$\tan \theta \text{ (or } a) = \frac{\text{opposite side}}{\text{adjacent side}}$$

In this case the hypotenuse (h) does not enter the equation.

Now, considering any angle θ, since

$$\sin \theta = \frac{\text{opp. side}}{h}, \quad \cos \theta = \frac{\text{adj. side}}{h}$$

then $\quad \dfrac{\sin \theta}{\cos \theta} = \dfrac{\text{opp. side}}{h} \times \dfrac{h}{\text{adj. side}} = \dfrac{\text{opp. side}}{\text{adj. side}} = \tan \theta$

Thus, as long as we remember that

$$\tan \theta = \frac{\sin \theta}{\cos \theta}$$

we need only to ensure remembering sin and cos to automatically recall tan.

EXAMPLE:
A pole AB stands on level ground. At 27.5 m away the pole is found to subtend an angle of 20° as in Fig. A3.2 (iii). What is the height of the pole?

$$\tan 20° = \frac{AB}{AC} = \frac{AB}{27.5}$$

∴　　　　　$AB = 27.5 \tan 20° = 27.5 \times 0.3640 = \underline{10 \text{ metres.}}$

EXAMPLE:
Draw an angle of 58° using a ruler only.

If we set up on squared paper AB and AC at rt. ∠s as in Fig. A3.2 (iv), in the ratio AC/AB of tan 58°, completion of the triangle gives the angle required.

$$\tan 58° = 1.6 \text{ (approx.)}$$

Draw AB, say, 10 cm, AC 10 × 1.6 = 16 cm, then

$$\angle ABC = 58°$$

To find the angle corresponding to a given value for a function (sin, cos or tan) the tables are used in reverse, for example, if sin θ = 0.7660, then θ = 50°. This is usually expressed

$$\sin^{-1} 0.7660 = 50° \quad \text{or} \quad \text{arc sin } 0.7660 = 50°$$

thus $\sin^{-1} x$ (or arc sin x) is the angle the sine of which is x

184

$\cos^{-1} x$ (or arc cos x) is the angle the cosine of which is x

$\tan^{-1} x$ (or arc tan x) is the angle the tangent of which is x

EXAMPLE:
Calculate $\angle ABC$ in Fig. A3.2 (iv) from AB = 10 cm, AC = 16 cm.

$$\tan \angle ABC = \frac{16}{10} = 1.6$$

$$\angle ABC = \tan^{-1} 1.6 = \underline{58°}$$

(the last line might also be written:

$$\angle ABC = \text{arc tan } 1.6 = 58°)$$

Now one warning: sin $(A + B)$ cannot be expanded as in ordinary algebra to sin A + sin B. In other words, sin, cos or tan, outside the bracket cannot be used as a multiplying factor is used. [If in doubt, always experiment, for example, is sin $(20° + 30°)$ equal to sin $20°$ + sin $30°$?]

A3.2.1 Angles greater than 90°

When the radius OR in Fig. A3.1 moves out of the 1st quadrant, the angle θ has a value greater than 90° extending in the 2nd quadrant up to 180°, in the 3rd from 180 – 270° and the 4th from 270 – 360°. As OR sweeps through each quadrant however, it is obvious that the rt. $\angle$d triangles it forms repeat for each quadrant, this is demonstrated in Fig. A3.3 where OR_1 has turned through 30° in the 1st quadrant producing opposite and adjacent sides $P_1 R_1$ and OP_1. Equally, when the radius is in the position OR_2 it has turned through 150° resulting in opposite and adjacent sides ($P_2 R_2$ and OP_2) equal to those in the first case because the angle within the rt. $\angle$d triangle is also 30°. Examination of Fig. A3.3 shows that the same conditions exist in the 3rd and 4th quadrants where OR_3 is at 210° and OR_4, 330°. Thus whatever the actual angle through which the radius has turned, we can always find its equivalent within the range $0 - 90°$ thus avoiding the need for more extensive tables. The rules for conversion are as follows:

If θ represents any angle through which the radius has turned,

    for 2nd quadrant use $180° - \theta$

    for 3rd quadrant use $\theta - 180°$

    for 4th quadrant use $360° - \theta$

as also marked on Fig. A3.3.

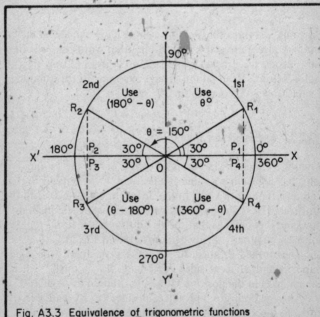

Fig. A3.3 Equivalence of trigonometric functions in the 4 quadrants.

EXAMPLE:
What are (i) sin 95°, (ii) sin 300°, (iii) cos 220°?

(i) 95° is in the 2nd quadrant therefore we look up in Table
     A3.1 sin (180° − 95°) = sin 85°, i.e. 0.9962;
(ii) 300° is in the 4th quadrant, (360° − 300°) applies, i.e.
     sin 60° = 0.8660;
(iii) 220° is in the 3rd quadrant, (220° − 180°) applies, i.e.
     cos 40° = 0.7660.

These are the figures given directly by trigonometrical tables,
they are not complete until their sign + or − has been added.
Much of our work is concerned with graphs[A2] so we
must adopt the same arrangement of values on the X and
Y axes, that is, considering the X-axis, positive values are to
the right of the Y-axis, negative values to the left. Considering the Y-axis, positive values are above the X-axis, negative
values below.

In Fig. A3.4 again let θ represent any angle through which the
radius OR has turned. Relative to OR as the hypotenuse, it
will be seen that the sine function is concerned with one other
side, PR, which is also the projection of OR on the Y-axis.
Sines therefore are positive or negative according to where this
projection lies on YY′, that is, sines of angles in the 1st and
2nd quadrants are positive because all projections of OR lie
on OY, they are negative in the 3rd and 4th quadrants because
they lie on OY′.

Similarly, cosines are concerned with the adjacent side which
always lies on the X-axis, thus cosines of angles in the 1st and
4th quadrants are positive, in the 2nd and 3rd quadrants,
negative. These are shown in the figure. Tangent polarities
may be determined similarly by considering both axes in each
quadrant together, thus

	X-axis		Y-axis		Tangent (Y/X)	
1st quadrant	X-axis	+	Y-axis	+	Tangent (Y/X)	+
2nd quadrant	″	−	″	+	″	−
3rd quadrant	″	−	″	−	″	+
4th quadrant	″	+	″	−	″	−

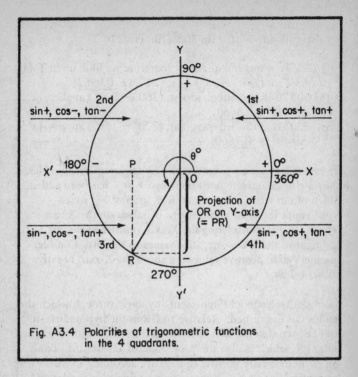

Fig. A3.4 Polarities of trigonometric functions in the 4 quadrants.

or equally by considering the polarities of sin/cos for the particular quadrant, e.g. 2nd quadrant, sin +, cos −, ∴ tan is +/−, i.e. − .

We can now complete the example:

(i) sin 85° = 0.9962 ∴ sin 95° = 0.9962 (sin is + in 2nd quadrant;

(ii) sin 60° = 0.8660 ∴ sin 300° = −0.8660 (sin is − in 4th quadrant;

(iii) cos 40° = 0.7660 ∴ cos 220° = −0.7660 (cos is − in 3rd quadrant).

By plotting graphs of the sine and cosine functions as obtained from Table A3.1 for 0 − 90° and as above for greater angles,

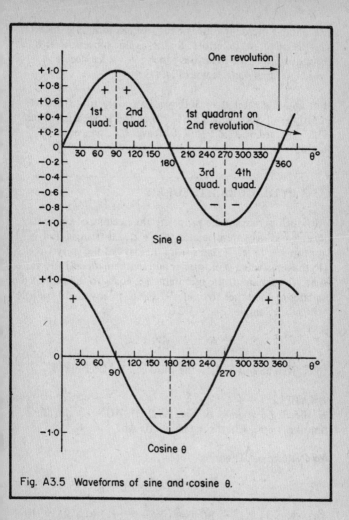

Fig. A3.5 Waveforms of sine and cosine θ.

the basic *sinusoidal* (wave-like) forms become apparent. These
are given in Fig. A3.5 and what is immediately evident is that
the two waves are identical in form, but the cosine is at a
maximum when the sine is zero and vice versa. The maximum
value for both is 1 since opposite and adjacent sides can only
increase up to the same value as the hypotenuse so giving a
ratio 1/1.

Recalling a mental picture of Fig. A3.5 is of help in memorizing the quadrant polarities, that is, as sine moves through the four quadrants the polarities run $+ + - -$, for cosine, $+ - - +$ which naturally agrees with Fig. A3.4.

For angles greater than 360° we have only to discard all multiples of 360° which are less than the angle, e.g. for tan 785°, discard 360° x 2 = 720° leaves 65°, hence tan 785° = tan 65°.

A3.3 PYTHAGORAS' THEOREM

Although perhaps more proper to the heading of Geometry, Pythagoras' Theorem relates to the rt. ∠d triangle and is appropriate here. It dates from the days of the early Greeks (Pythagoras was a philosopher and mathematician) and states that "the square of the hypotenuse is equal to the sum of the squares of the other two sides", that is, in any rt. ∠d triangle ABC, for example, Fig. A3.2 (i)

$$AC^2 = AB^2 + BC^2 ,$$

thus given any two sides, the third can be determined.

EXAMPLE:
In the rt. ∠d triangle of Fig. A3.2 (i), AC = 10 cm, BC is approx. 9 cm. What is the length of AB?

By Pythagoras' Theorem

$$AC^2 = AB^2 + BC^2$$

$$\therefore \quad AB^2 = AC^2 - BC^2 = 10^2 - 9^2 = 100 - 81 = 19$$

$$\therefore \quad AB = \sqrt{19} = \underline{4.36 \text{ cm.}}$$

EXAMPLE:

For the triangle of Fig. A3.2 (iv), calculate the length of BC.

(i)   By Pythagoras' Theorem:

$$BC^2 = 16^2 + 10^2 \therefore BC = \sqrt{256 + 100} = \sqrt{356} =$$

$$= \underline{18.87 \text{ cm.}}$$

(ii)   By Trigonometry:

$$\frac{AC}{BC} = \sin 58° \therefore BC = \frac{AC}{\sin 58°} = \frac{16}{0.848} = \underline{18.87 \text{ cm}}$$

or

$$\frac{AB}{BC} = \cos 58° \therefore BC = \frac{AB}{\cos 58°} = \frac{10}{0.5299} = \underline{18.87 \text{ cm.}}$$

TABLE A3.1   Trigonometric functions

ANGLE (degrees)	SINE	COSINE	TANGENT
0	0	1.0000	0
1	0.0175	0.9998	0.0175
2	.0349	.9994	.0349
3	.0523	.9986	.0524
4	.0698	.9976	.0699
5	.0872	.9962	.0875
6	.1045	.9945	.1051
7	.1219	.9925	.1228
8	.1392	.9903	.1405
9	.1564	.9877	.1584
10	.1736	.9848	.1763
11	.1908	.9816	.1944
12	.2079	.9781	.2126
13	.2250	.9744	.2309
14	.2419	.9703	.2493
15	.2588	.9659	.2679
16	.2756	.9613	.2867
17	.2924	.9563	.3057
18	.3090	.9511	.3249
19	.3256	.9455	.3443
20	.3420	.9397	.3640
21	.3584	.9336	.3839
22	.3746	.9272	.4040
23	.3907	.9205	.4245
24	.4067	.9135	.4452
25	.4226	.9063	.4663
26	.4384	.8988	.4877
27	.4540	.8910	.5095
28	.4695	.8829	.5317
29	.4848	.8746	.5543
30	.5000	.8660	.5774

TABLE A3.1 continued

ANGLE (degrees)	SINE	COSINE	TANGENT
31	0.5150	0.8572	0.6009
32	.5299	.8480	.6249
33	.5446	.8387	.6494
34	.5592	.8290	.6745
35	.5736	.8192	.7002
36	.5878	.8090	.7265
37	.6018	.7986	.7536
38	.6157	.7880	.7813
39	.6293	.7771	.8098
40	.6428	.7660	.8391
41	.6561	.7547	.8693
42	.6691	.7431	.9004
43	.6820	.7314	.9325
44	.6947	.7193	.9657
45	.7071	.7071	1.0000
46	.7193	.6947	1.0355
47	.7314	.6820	1.0724
48	.7431	.6691	1.1106
49	.7547	.6561	1.1504
50	.7660	.6428	1.1918
51	.7771	.6293	1.2349
52	.7880	.6157	1.2799
53	.7986	.6018	1.3270
54	.8090	.5878	1.3764
55	.8192	.5736	1.4281
56	.8290	.5592	1.4826
57	.8387	.5446	1.5399
58	.8480	.5299	1.6003
59	.8572	.5150	1.6643
60	.8660	.5000	1.7321

TABLE A3.1 continued

ANGLE (degrees)	SINE	COSINE	TANGENT
61	0.8746	0.4848	1.8040
62	.8829	.4695	1.8807
63	.8910	.4540	1.9626
64	.8988	.4384	2.0503
65	.9063	.4226	2.1445
66	.9135	.4067	2.2460
67	.9205	.3907	2.3559
68	.9272	.3746	2.4751
69	.9336	.3584	2.6051
70	.9397	.3420	2.7475
71	.9455	.3256	2.9042
72	.9511	.3090	3.0777
73	.9563	.2924	3.2709
74	.9613	.2756	3.4874
75	.9659	.2588	3.7321
76	.9703	.2419	4.0108
77	.9744	.2250	4.3315
78	.9781	.2079	4.7046
79	.9816	.1908	5.1446
80	.9848	.1736	5.6713
81	.9877	.1564	6.3138
82	.9903	.1392	7.1154
83	.9925	.1219	8.1443
84	.9945	.1045	9.5144
85	.9962	.0872	11.4301
86	.9976	.0698	14.3007
87	.9986	.0523	19.0811
88	.9994	.0349	28.6363
89	.9998	.0175	57.2900
90	1.0000	0	∞

APPENDIX 4

MATHEMATICS

The mathematics appropriate to earlier studies are contained in Book 1. The following concepts are important in extending the techniques of analysis of electronic circuits which are contained in this book.

A4.1 VECTORS

The statement that an aircraft is flying at 500 km/h gives information on its speed or rate of travel only, we do not know in which direction it is flying. This quantity, like those representing time, length, weight, area, temperature, etc., is known as a *scalar* quantity for it is fully expressed by a single number. If directional information is added, say, the aircraft is flying South, we have then created a *vector* quantity which involves both magnitude and direction. In specifying the latter an angle with some reference is involved, for the aircraft, the reference is known world-wide as North and labelled $0°$, thus the direction South is completely specified by the figure $180°$. Diagrammatically a vector quantity is illustrated by a line of definite length representing the magnitude and drawn at the appropriate angle and with an arrow added, to represent the direction. Thus the aircraft vector would be as in Fig. A4.1, a line of length, say, 5 cm pointing downwards on the paper.

For navigation this single vector does not tell the whole story because aircraft must take into account the effects of air-currents while ships are affected by both sea and air-currents. But vectors can be added geometrically so the navigator has all that is needed to find the net effect of all forces acting and hence determine the true direction.

Consider a West to East wind having a speed of, say, 100 km/h affecting the aircraft. The vector is as shown in (ii) indicating

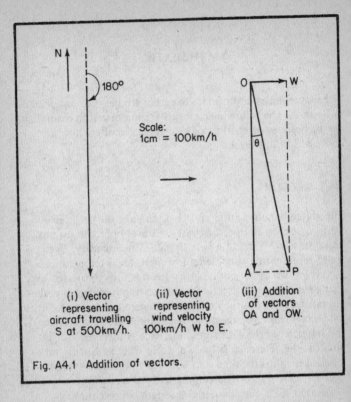

(i) Vector representing aircraft travelling S at 500km/h.

(ii) Vector representing wind velocity 100km/h W to E.

(iii) Addition of vectors OA and OW.

Fig. A4.1 Addition of vectors.

how the air surrounding the aircraft is moving, in this case causing it to have a velocity sideways from its intended track. To find the actual path taken by the aircraft the two vectors are added by completion of the parallelogram (a 4-sided figure with opposite sides parallel) as shown in (iii). In this particular case and in many we meet in electronics the two vectors are at 90° to each other and the parallelogram therefore becomes a rectangle.

We imagine the aircraft to be at point O. It has two velocities OA, its own and OW, that of the air. The rectangle OAPW is completed and the diagonal (the line joining opposite corners) drawn. It is the diagonal which is the vector representing the resultant of the other two, that is, it shows the actual velocity (both speed and direction) of the aircraft. OP and $\angle\theta$ can be measured or calculated.

By calculation, because OAP is at rt.$\angle$d triangle, we can use Pythagoras' Theorem[A3.3], then

$$OP^2 = OA^2 + AP^2 \text{ , but } AP = OW$$

$$\therefore \quad OP^2 = 500^2 + 100^2 = 250,000 + 10,000 = 260,000$$

$$\therefore \quad OP = \sqrt{260,000} = \underline{509.9 \text{ km/h.}}$$

Also

$$\tan \theta^{[A3.2]} = \frac{100}{500} = 0.2$$

$$\therefore \quad\quad\quad \theta \approx 11.5°$$

(Full trigonometric tables give the answer as 11°19′; at 1° intervals only, the tables in Appendix 3 give a slightly less accurate answer.)

Relative to North, the actual aircraft flight track is 180° − 11.5° = 168.5°.

EXAMPLE:
A ship is sailing at 4 knots apparently in a NE direction, but there is a sea current flowing SE at 3 knots. What is the actual velocity of the ship relative to the ocean bed?

NE is at a angle of 45° relative to N, and SE is at an angle of 135° relative to N.

The vector diagram is as shown in Fig. A4.2.

Let OS represent the sailing velocity and OC represent the sea current velocity.

197

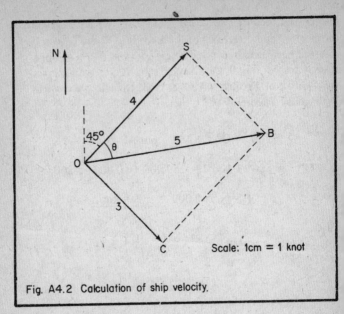

Fig. A4.2 Calculation of ship velocity.

Then OB represents the velocity of the ship relative to the ocean bed.

By Pythagoras' Theorem:

$$OB^2 = OC^2 + OS^2 = 4^2 + 3^2 = 16 + 9 = 25$$

$$\therefore \qquad OB = \sqrt{25} = \underline{5 \text{ knots.}}$$

(Here we meet the well-known 3, 4, 5 triangle, an easy-to-remember combination of sides.)

$$\tan \theta = \frac{BS}{OS} = \frac{3}{4} = 0.75$$

$$\therefore \qquad \theta \approx 37°$$

i.e. the ship actually moves relative to the ocean bed at 5 knots in a direction at 45 + 37 = $\underline{82°}$ (relative to North).

A4.1.1 Resolution of Vectors

Just as we can combine two vectors and find their resultant, so
equally we can take a vector and resolve it into two components, usually, and especially in the case of electronics, at rt ∠s
to each other. Thus in Fig. A4.3 the vector OP can be *resolved*
into two components mutually at rt. ∠s, OA and OB which,
acting together, could replace it.

If $\angle AOP = \theta$, then $\angle OPB = \theta$, and

$$OA = OP \cos \theta$$

$$OB = OP \sin \theta ,$$

and these relationships hold whatever angle we choose for θ.

Also since

$$\angle BOP = (90 - \theta)^{\circ} = a^{\circ}$$

then, $$OB = OP \cos (90 - \theta)^{\circ} = OP \cos a^{\circ}$$

giving the general conclusion that the resolved part of a vector
in any given direction is equal to the magnitude of the vector
multiplied by the cosine of the angle it makes with that
direction.

The rule can be demonstrated practically by referring to the

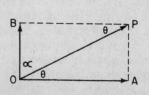

Fig. A4.3 Resolution of vector.

199

last example illustrated by Fig. A4.2. We now resolve the vector OB into its two components at rt. ∠s, given that the angle OB makes with one of the parts, OS, is 37°. Then ∠COB = (90 − 37)° = 53°. Hence

$$OS = 5 \cos 37° = 4 \text{ knots}$$

$$OC = 5 \cos 53° = 3 \text{ knots}$$

which we know to be correct.

A4.1.2 Phasors

Within a vector quantity is visible direction, for example, one can see the direction in which a body moves, more precisely the vector is said to have a dimension in space. In alternating current theory much use is made of vectors having a dimension in time, illustrated by Fig. 1.3 in the main text where OR is in fact a vector because it has both magnitude and direction. Its direction is expressed by the angle through which it has rotated from a reference point. Such vectors are known as *phasors* and although the work is done in angles for convenience, we must never forget that these actually represent differences in time. There is ample illustration of the use of phasors in the main text.

A4.2 EPSILON

This is a term we shall meet constantly throughout electronics and communication. It is the name of the Greek letter ϵ but we usually use the English letter e as our symbol. It has a very odd-looking value, 2.71818281828 . . . simply because this is the way things work out when we put numbers to Nature, for not only does epsilon appear in our own electronic considerations, but also in the absorption of light, cooling of a body, atmospheric pressure and a host of other *natural* phenomena. π, the ratio of the circumference to the diameter of a circle also does not give us a simple, convenient number, but we have to live with this.

Epsilon enters the scene whenever an increment in any quantity that is growing is proportional to the magnitude of the quantity itself at that time. Similarly, for any quantity decreasing in magnitude and each decrease being proportional to that magnitude. An example from everyday life is heat loss. A kettle which has just boiled loses heat much more rapidly than one which is only just warm, more exactly its heat loss is proportional to the excess of its temperature above that of the air surrounding it and mathematically its "cooling curve", that is, graph of temperature against time, involves epsilon.

A second example is that of money invested at *compound interest*, where the interest earned and added at the end of each period to the amount invested is proportional to the total amount of money invested plus accrued interest at the beginning of the period. The increment is proportional to the magnitude of the quantity which is growing. We can therefore use compound interest to get a little closer to epsilon.

Simple interest is described by its name. We lend somebody our £100 and they pay us so much per cent per annum for the privilege of having the use of our money. If the rate of interest is, say, 8% per annum, then after 1 year we receive £8 on our £100, after 2 years, a further £8 making a total of $2 \times 8 = £16$, and so on. So after, say, 5 years we still have our £100 to be returned some day and have received a total of $5 \times 8 = £40$ simple interest.

But suppose our borrower agreed to use the interest as fast as it was generated, we should then be lending him a sum which is increasing annually, thus:

Amount originally invested (or loaned)   = £100
Interest at end of first year = £$(100 \times 8/100)$ = £   8
∴ Total amount at end of first year =

$$£100 + £(100 \times 8/100) = £100(1 + 8/100) \quad = £108$$

and as a general formula we get:

$$P(1 + r/100)$$

where P is the *principal* and r is the (annual) rate of interest showing that in a year the principal grows by the factor $(1 + r/100)$. In the 2nd year it grows by the same factor:

∴ Total amount at end of 2nd year =

$$£100(1 + 8/100)(1 + 8/100) \qquad = £116.64$$

i.e. 64p more interest than for simple interest over the 2 years.

If we continue the process we find when substituting r for the rate of interest per *period* and n for the number of those periods,

Amount to which the principal P grows = $\underline{P(1 + r/100)^n}$

e.g. after 5 years at 8% per annum compound interest our £100 becomes

$$£100(1 + 8/100)^5 = £100 \times 1.08^5 = £146.93.$$

Here, n, the number of periods is 5 because the interest is added annually. If however it is added quarterly, n becomes 20 and r becomes 2% per quarter and we would get

$$£100(1 + 2/100)^{20} = £100 \times 1.02^{20} = £148.59,$$

so that in changing from yearly to quarterly, the interest rate has been divided by 4, the period multiplied by the same number and there is slightly more interest.

True compound interest means continuously adding interest to the amount which is growing (rather like pouring in a continuous trickle of water instead of a bucketful periodically) thus the period becomes infinitely small and the number by which we divide the interest rate and multiply the period, infinitely large, our expression thus changing to the general one

$$P(1 + 1/\infty)^\infty$$

[some notes on ∞, infinity, are given at the end of this Appendix].

This has not explained why r has been lost from the formula (but note that r is of little account when divided by infinity) but this slight simplification is for the sake of brevity and we leave the money question at this point for it has now usefully introduced us to epsilon which is calculated from the expression $(1 + 1/\infty)^\infty$, i.e.

$$e = (1 + 1/\infty)^\infty$$

an expression which appears to be useless since $1/\infty = 0$, $\therefore$ $e = 1^\infty = 1$ which we know is incorrect. However, mathematicians are able to solve this and it is actually calculated out from a series developed from the *Binomial Theorem* ("binomial" because there are two terms within the bracket). We cannot develop this here, nor should we because it only adds further unnecessary complication to an already difficult concept. Sufficient to say that

$$e = (1 + 1/\infty)^\infty = 1 + 1 + \frac{1}{2!} + \frac{1}{3!} + \frac{1}{4!} + \frac{1}{5!} + \frac{1}{6!} + \ldots$$

$$= 2.718281828$$

Each of the denominators is called a *factorial*, that is 3!, 4!, 7!, etc., are expressed as factorial 3, factorial 4, factorial 7, etc., simply meaning $3 \times 2 \, (\times 1)$, $\quad 4 \times 3 \times 2$, $7 \times 6 \times 5 \times 4 \times 3 \times 2$, etc.

Theoretically the series has an infinite number of terms but we do not need many to calculate a reasonable approximation to e as shown in the following example.

EXAMPLE:
Calculate the approximate value of e from the first 9 terms of the series.

$$\text{Approx. value of } e = 1 + 1 + \frac{1}{2!} + \frac{1}{3!} + \frac{1}{4!} + \frac{1}{5!} + \frac{1}{6!} + \frac{1}{7!} + \frac{1}{8!}$$

$$= 2.5 + \frac{1}{6} + \frac{1}{24} + \frac{1}{120} + \frac{1}{720} + \frac{1}{5040} + \frac{1}{40320}$$

$$= 2.5 + 0.16667 + 0.04167 + 0.00833 + 0.00139$$

$$+ 0.00020 + 0.00002$$

$$= \underline{2.71828}$$

The graphs of many natural phenomena involve *exponential functions* of e. An exponential function or just "exponential" is one which has one of the variable quantities in the exponent (or index) of another quantity, for example, in $y = k^{2x}$ ($y = k$ to the $2x$), x is a variable quantity in the exponent of k, a constant. We can vary x if we wish to see what happens to y, hence x is called the *independent variable,* and y, which depends on the value assigned to x, the *dependent variable.*

In electronics $y = e^{-t/CR}$ has t (time) as the independent variable, e being constant and C and R constant for a particular circuit. The minus sign in the exponent makes the term into its reciprocal, i.e.

$$y = e^{-t/CR} \text{ is the same as } y = \frac{1}{e^{t/CR}}$$

A4.2.1 Calculation of e^x

Books of tables almost invariably contain common logarithms (base = 10) but some have also *Natural Logarithms* (base = e, also known as *Napierian Logarithms*, after John Napier, a Scottish mathematician). With the latter, since x is the natural logarithm of the number we require, we simply look up the antilog of x in the tables, for example

$$e^{1.075} = 2.93 \text{ because } \log_e 2.93 = 1.075$$

The fortunate reader who owns a scientific calculator may decide to read no further in this section although what follows still offers good practice with logarithms and exponentials.

Having now introduced e as a base for logarithmic tables we must be careful to indicate which base is being used at any particular time. Just to refresh our memories, let us calculate a simple, known multiplication such as 1.9 x 3 (= 5.7) using both common and natural logarithmic tables, after which we will calculate e^x using common logarithms only.

$$\log_{10} 1.9 \qquad = 0.2788$$
$$\log_{10} 3.0 \qquad = 0.4771$$
$$\overline{}$$
$$\log_{10}(1.9 \times 3.0) \qquad = 0.7559$$

$\therefore \quad (1.9 \times 3.0) = \text{antilog}_{10} 0.7559 = \underline{5.7}$

$$\log_e 1.9 \qquad = 0.6419$$
$$\log_e 3.0 \qquad = 1.0986$$
$$\overline{}$$
$$\log_e(1.9 \times 3.0) \qquad = 1.7405$$

$\therefore \quad (1.9 \times 3.0) = \text{antilog}_e 1.7405 = \underline{5.7}$

so demonstrating that logarithmic tables to any base are equally effective.

Natural logarithmic tables are not essential, however, for if we let x represent any power of e and y the unknown value so that $y = e^x$ then we can first take common logs of both sides, giving

$$\log_{10} y = \log_{10} e^x$$

furthermore, to find the log of any number raised to a power, the log of the number is multiplied by that power, i.e.

$$\log_{10} e^{x} = x \log_{10} e$$

[Logarithms and their manipulation often give rise to confusion — if in any doubt, always stop and check using simple numbers, for example in place of e^{x} use, say 3^{4} and is $\log_{10} 3^{4}$ the same as $4 \times \log_{10} 3$? It is, because $\log_{10} 3^{4} = \log_{10} 81 = 1.9085$ and $4 \times \log_{10} 3 = 4 \times 0.4771 = 1.9084$, the small discrepancy being due to the slight inaccuracies which may occur with 4-figure logs.]

Then $$\log_{10} y = x \log_{10} e$$

Now $$e = 2.718 \text{ and } \log_{10} e = 0.4343$$

∴ $$\log_{10} y = x \times 0.4343$$

and taking antilogs of both sides:

$$y = \text{antilog}_{10}(x \times 0.4343)$$

i.e. $$\underline{e^{x} = \text{antilog}_{10}(x \times 0.4343)}$$

EXAMPLE:
Calculate the value of $e^{1.075}$:

$$e^{1.075} = \text{antilog}_{10}(1.075 \times 0.4343)$$

[The figures in the brackets may be multiplied together by any method, including logarithms, e.g.

$\log_{10} 1.075$	$= 0.0314$
$\log_{10} 0.4343$	$= \bar{1}.6378$
$\log_{10}$ of product	$= \bar{1}.6692$

Product $= \text{antilog}_{10} \bar{1}.6692 = 0.4669$.]

$$\therefore \qquad e^{1.075} = \text{antilog}_{10}\,0.4669 = \underline{2.93}$$

as found at the beginning of this section using natural log tables.

EXAMPLE:

Calculate the value of $e^{-0.8}$

$$e^{-0.8} = \text{antilog}_{10}\,(-0.8 \times 0.4343)$$

$$= \text{antilog}_{10}(-0.3474)$$

$$= \text{antilog}_{10}\,\bar{1}.6526$$

$$= \underline{0.4493}$$

A4.2.2   Natural Logarithms from Common

To find a natural logarithm when only common logarithm tables are available, let $y = \log_e x$, then

$$e^y = x$$

and taking common logs of both sides,

$$\log_{10} e^y = \log_{10} x$$

$$\therefore \qquad y \log_{10} e = \log_{10} x$$

$$\therefore \qquad y = \frac{\log_{10} x}{\log_{10} e} = \frac{\log_{10} x}{0.4343} = \log_{10} x \times 2.3026$$

i.e. the natural log of any number x is given by

$$\frac{\log_{10} x}{0.4343} \quad \text{or} \quad \log_{10} x \times 2.3026$$

EXAMPLE:
Find the natural logarithm of π using common logarithm tables.

$$\log_e \pi = \log_{10} \pi \times 2.3026$$

$$= \log_{10} 3.142 \times 2.3026$$

$= 0.4972 \times 2.3026 \quad \rightarrow \quad \log_{10} 0.4972 \qquad = \overline{1}.6966$
$\log_{10} 2.303 \qquad = 0.3623$

$\log_{10}$ of product $\qquad = 0.0589$
$\therefore \underline{\log_e \pi = 1.145} \qquad \leftarrow \quad$ antilog $\qquad = 1.145$

A4.3 RATE OF CHANGE

As we increase our acquaintance with ac theory, it becomes evident that time enters the reasoning more and more and not only time itself but also how quickly or slowly things change with it.

Using inductance as a typical example, the induced emf e (nothing to do with epsilon in the preceding sections) can be calculated from

$$e = L \times (\text{rate of change of current}) = L \times \frac{i_2 - i_1}{t}$$

showing that e depends on the rate (or speed) at which the current changes from i_1 to i_2, for example, if a change occurs in half the time, the rate is doubled and so is e. Thus e depends not only on the current change itself but also on the time it takes to change. The rate in this particular case is expressed in amperes per second (A/s).

If the graph of a quantity y against time is a straight line, as in Fig. A4.4 (i) then the rate of change of y with time is the same whatever the actual value of time. Between t_1 and t_2 the rise in y is $(y_2 - y_1)$ and if we label $(t_2 - t_1)$ as δt (Greek, delta) and $(y_2 - y_1)$ as δy where δ means "a small change in" then the rate of increase in y is $\delta y/\delta t$ (i.e. a small change in y divided by the small change in t required for it to happen).

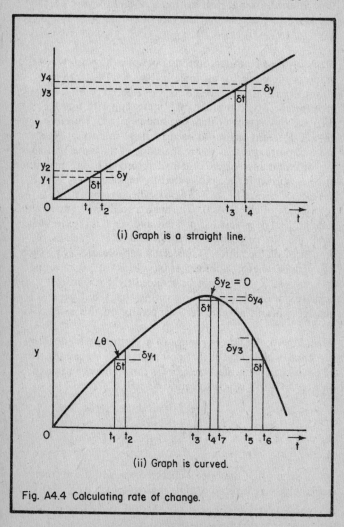

(i) Graph is a straight line.

(ii) Graph is curved.

Fig. A4.4 Calculating rate of change.

Because the graph is a straight line, a similar time interval taken at a later time, e.g. $(t_4 - t_3)$, at which time y rises by $(y_4 - y_3)$ gives a rate of change of y also as $\delta y/\delta t$. Again because the graph is a straight line, it is not necessary to take time intervals over a small section but valid to work over the whole of the graph so that the rate of change of y is equally given by $(y_4 - 0)/(t_4 - 0)$.

Many of these considerations do not apply however when the graph is curved as for example in Fig. A4.4 (ii). Here, although each time interval δt is the same, δy_1, δy_2, δy_3 are all different, δy_1 is positive (y is increasing with time), δy_2 is zero and δy_3 is greater than δy_1 and negative. Thus $\delta y/\delta t$ gives a different answer at each of these intervals. What is more important is that where the slope of the curve is changing, different answers are obtained according to the magnitude of δt as shown for example, that by making δt $(t_7 - t_3)$ the rate of change of y is $\delta y_4/\delta t$, whereas when δt is $(t_4 - t_3)$ the rate of change is 0. The answer to this is to make the time interval δt as small as possible and when it is extremely small the rate of change is written as dy/dt. Calculus, a branch of mathematics, is especially capable of solving such expressions when δt approaches 0 (written $\delta t \to 0$, meaning δt is almost 0 — it cannot be reduced right down to 0 because nothing happens to y in no time), but we must manage without another large appendix on this subject.

When $\delta t \to 0$, the rate of change of y with time is equal to the slope of the curve at that point and if the slope is expressed as an angle with the time axis (as shown between t_2 and t_1 on Fig. A4.4 (ii), where the curve slope is $\theta°$), then

$$\tan \theta = \frac{dy_1}{dt}$$

which means that the rate of change of y with t over that extremely small interval of time is given by $\tan \theta$.

A.4.4 INFINITY

Sometimes difficult to appreciate because we never actually get there, also who can avoid a sense of confusion on being told that parallel lines meet at infinity when it would appear that they never meet at all?

Infinite (Latin, "infinitus", unbounded) according to the dictionary means "having no limit or end, boundless, immeasurably great in extent, duration, etc." We could ourselves perhaps add to this "immeasurably small" for we frequently talk of infinitely small increments which now brings us also into contact with *zero*, a better understood term. The linking of infinity (symbol ∞) with zero (symbol 0, "nought") is simply demonstrated by reciprocals as follows.

The reciprocal of the number or decimal fraction 0.1 is 10, of 0.001 it is 1000 and of 0.000001 it is 1,000,000. As the number diminishes its reciprocal becomes larger and as the process continues the strings of noughts get longer — through the vast expanse of increasing nothingness on the one hand and increasing enormity on the other. Much of this is of no use in the practical world but must be traversed to reach the mathematical points of 0 and ∞ for at the limit, when the number is actually 0, the reciprocal has become infinitely large or "infinity". Thus

$$\frac{1}{0} = \infty \quad \text{and} \quad \frac{1}{\infty} = 0$$

Clearly infinity is more a theoretical than a practical concept because in many instances the difference made in a result by considering a large number or alternatively an infinitely large one is negligible. Two examples follow in illustration:

(i)   theoretically a capacitor needs infinite time to charge fully, in practice it is considered to be charged after a time equal to five time-constants, usually a matter of seconds (Sect. 2.2);

211

(ii)   the series for calculating epsilon theoretically needs an
        infinite number of terms, we manage extremely well
        with less than 20 (Appendix 4.2),

and these examples show that we should not be too inflexible
in our minds when infinity is embodied in the discussion.

APPENDIX 5

GEOMETRY

A5.1 THE PARALLELOGRAM

This is a four-sided figure, the opposite sides of which are parallel (that is, continuously equidistant) as shown in Fig. A5.1. AB and DC are parallel, also AD and BC are parallel and in fact it could be said that a parallelogram is formed when one pair of parallel lines intersects with another pair.

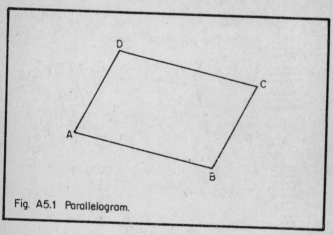

Fig. A5.1 Parallelogram.

Should one of the angles be a rt. $\angle$, it follows that the other three are also and the figure, although technically still a parallelogram, is known as a rectangle, or if adjacent sides are equal, a square.

In electronics we are usually confronted with two "phasors" acting from a point at some angle to each other. As far as we are concerned here, these are simply two lines meeting to form adjacent sides of a parallelogram. The resultant of the two phasors is found by "completing the parallelogram" (i.e. adding the remaining two sides) and drawing the diagonal.

To do this we must first be able to draw a line parallel to a given line.

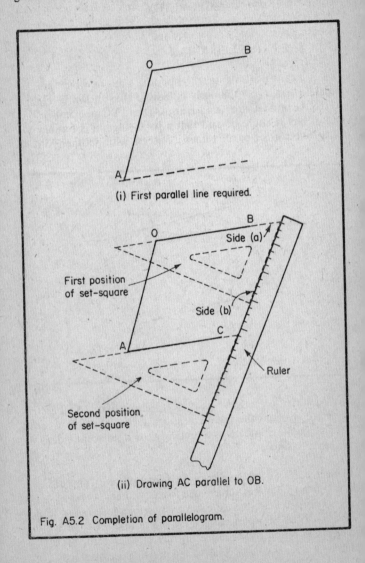

(i) First parallel line required.

(ii) Drawing AC parallel to OB.

Fig. A5.2 Completion of parallelogram.

Suppose the two lines OA and OB (representing phasors) are at some angle as shown in Fig. A5.2 (i) and it is required to complete the parallelogram. We have first to draw a line from A parallel to OB as shown dotted. This is most easily accomplished using a set-square and a ruler:

(i)   one side (a) of the set-square is lined up with OB as shown in Fig. A5.2 (ii);

(ii) a ruler is then placed in contact with side (b) and held in this position;

(iii) the set-square is slid down the ruler until its side (a) meets the end A of OA, the required line AC is then drawn from A along the (a) edge.

The process is then repeated with the set-square lined up to OA and the line from B parallel to OA drawn. The intersection of the two lines drawn completes the parallelogram.

A few trials may first be required in choosing the best edge of the set-square to use.

MOVING INTO BOOK 3

Books 1 and 2 have built the foundation on which Book 3 rests. Nobody can really feel at home with transistors and integrated circuits unless possessing some insight into the motivation of electrons and acquaintance with what happens in a circuit when voltages or currents change.

Thus the reader is now well prepared for the next step into a world ever diminishing in size but greatly expanding in accomplishment — a world of transistors, amplifiers, oscillators, switching and logic circuits, power supplies and micro-miniature technology.

Please note overleaf is a list of other titles that are available in our range of Radio and Electronics Books.

These should be available from most good Booksellers, Radio Component Dealers and Mail Order Companies.

However, should you experience difficulty in obtaining any title in your area, then please write directly to the publishers enclosing payment to cover the cost of the book plus adequate postage.

If you would like a copy of our latest catalogue of Radio and Electronics Books then please send a Stamped Addressed Envelope to:—

BERNARD BABANI (publishing) LTD
The Grampians
Shepherds Bush Road
London W6 7NF
England.